PROGRAMMABLE CONTROLLER CIRCUITS

Roger M. Bertrand
Central Maine Technical College

Delmar Publishers

I(T)P™ An International Thomson Publishing Company

Albany • Bonn • Boston • Cincinnati • Detroit • London • Madrid • Melbourne
Mexico City • New York • Pacific Grove • Paris • San Francisco • Singapore • Tokyo
Toronto • Washington

NOTICE TO THE READER

Cover Design: Courtesy of Charles Cummings Advertising/Art Inc.

Delmar Staff
Publisher: Susan Simpfenderfer
Project Development Editor: Michelle Ruelos Cannistraci
Production Coordinator: Karen Smith

COPYRIGHT © 1996
By Delmar Publishers
a division of International Thomson Publishing Inc.
The ITP logo is a trademark under license

Printed in the United States of America

For more information contact:

Delmar Publishers
3 Columbia Circle, Box 15015
Albany, New York 12212-5015

International Thomson Publishing Europe
Berkshire House 168–173
High Holborn
London WC1V 7AA
England

Thomas Nelson Australia
102 Dodds Street
South Melbourne, 3205
Victoria, Australia

Nelson Canada
1120 Birchmount Road
Scarborough, Ontario
Canada M1K 5G4

International Thomson Editores
Campos Eliseos 385, Piso 7
Col Polanco
11560 Mexico D F Mexico

International Thomson Publishing GmbH
Königswinterer Strasse 418
53227 Bonn
Germany

International Thomson Publishing Asia
221 Henderson Road
#05–10 Henderson Building
Singapore 0315

International Thomson Publishing-Japan
Hirakawacho Kyowa Building, 3F
2-2-1 Hirakawacho
Chiyoda-ku, Tokyo 102
Japan

1 2 3 4 5 6 7 8 9 10 XXX 10 00 99 98 97 96 95

Library of Congress Cataloging-in-Publication Data

Bertrand, Roger M.
    Programmable controller circuits / Roger M. Bertrand.
        p.   cm.
    ISBN 0-8273-7066-0
    1. Electronic controllers—Design and construction.   2. Logic
circuits—Design and construction.   3. Process control—Experiments.
I. Title.
TK7881.2.B465   1995   95-17503
629.8'9—dc20   CIP

CONTENTS

PREFACE

This book is a project/lab manual designed to provide instruction and practical laboratory experience for the student of industrial controls. Its purposes are twofold: (1) To provide a background on programming control circuits and concepts that are used in industry and (2) to provide structured laboratory experiences based on industrial applications.

The first section covers electromechanical motor controls. Projects 1 through 4 focus on connecting motor starters, relays, pushbuttons, roto-push units, selector switches, and timers. Project 5 deals with the programming of an adjustable frequency AC drive. There are numerous control circuits that are used in typical motor control applications. These common types of circuits will be used throughout this project manual.

The major emphasis of the manual is in the second section, Projects 6 through 24, which are PLC programming sections encompassing a wide range of programming projects. The projects are designed to progress through various stages of instruction and how they function together as a control system. Applications include instructions such as relay, timers, counters, comparison, conversion, file, shift register, sequencers, ADC, DAC, process control and structured text.

Throughout the manual, students will construct and program their own circuits focusing on "real world" purposes. The projects and experiments will lead them in a step-by-step development process designed to progress through various stages of programming instructions. The students' abilities to analyze and program circuits will progress as they complete each project.

Although the projects in this manual were designed and completed with the Allen-Bradley PLC-5, 6200 software, each project is written with clear objectives and step-by-step procedures. Using the manufacturer's instructions and manuals appropriate to the equipment, plus following the program objectives, one can apply other makes of PLCs to complete the projects.

FEATURES

The projects all have a similar format. Each one begins with a set of *objectives* which state the goals and define the principle ideas of the project.

The *reference reading section* directs students to the appropriate sections of instruction references located in the appendix. The *programming section* of the project manual is intended to complement the Allen-Bradley PLC-5, instruction set reference manual.

The *discussion section* provides background information on the project, including the characteristics of the instructions used in the program. In addition, the special programming features of the circuit are pointed out.

The *program logic section* shows the sequence of operation of the project, including some of the key instructions needed to implement the project circuit.

The *procedure section* details a step by step procedure for completing the project. It also demonstrates various programming instructions or a detailed circuit on the project.

The *experiment section* develops additional skills in analyzing and programming other similar type of circuits. The experiments, where applicable, challenge the comprehension of the information in that project.

The *appendixes* located at the end of the text assists the students. Appendix A is an instruction set quick reference table. The table shows an example of each instruction used in the PLC-5 processors. These examples show actual instructions, addresses and a brief description of each example. Appendix B includes information on programming-entering and editing SFCs and components for the ROTO-PUSH® units.

SUPPLEMENT

An *instructor's guide* is also available. The guide provides additional information such as course syllabus, intended usage, instructor tips and program solutions. Included in the instructors guide is information on how to build a low-voltage project simulator. The low-voltage simulator can be used to complete all of the programming projects and experiments in this project manual. The simulator and the input/output modules are all controlled with 24 volts DC. The low-voltage ensures a safer working environment for the students.

The simulator and I/O chassis system can be as complicated as one can afford or wants to build. Two options are described: (1) A simpler approach using one chassis and one assembled simulator and (2) a broader approach using a main chassis with a low-voltage simulator along with a remote chassis to provide for additional projects. With the supervision of the instructor, this simulator station can be assembled and connected by students to provide valuable training in the process.

ACKNOWLEDGMENTS

This final product is a result of the efforts of many people including the reviewers, the students who spent many hours completing the projects, and the editorial and production people at Delmar.

I want to express my appreciation to the following reviewers:

William Frayer, Central Maine Technical College, for his technical writing suggestions

Richard Ouellette, System Design Integrators

David V. Jones, Lenoir Community College

James Ahneman, Chippewa Technical College

I would like to dedicate this book to my son Craig.

ELECTROMECHANICAL

In this section, the projects will familiarize you with electromechanical devices and ladder logic diagrams. Examples of ladder logic are presented to provide a basic idea of how the circuits can be used in practical situations. The emphasis throughout the text is placed on using low voltage controls to provide a safer learning environment. Today, programmable controllers have replaced many electromechanical relays and timers. However, the same logical analysis is still valid, and a basic knowledge of this area is essential to the understanding of programming techniques.

OBJECTIVES

After completing this section, you should be able to:
- Design and connect ladder diagrams showing the proper logic relationship of inputs and outputs.
- Construct control circuits using pushbuttons and full-voltage motor starters.
- Investigate the basic laws and rules of the National Electrical Code pertaining to motor control circuits.
- Implement roto-push selector switches to various logic systems.
- Analyze timer-on and timer-off delay circuits and apply them to industrial control circuits.
- Understand the use of overloads in a three–phase motor starter.
- Set up various forward and reverse control circuits to produce specified sequences.
- Interpret data sheets of industrial motor control catalogs.
- Select the proper IEC low voltage coil starters.
- Recognize and connect programmable controller input and output modules.
- Program the various parameters of an adjustable frequency AC drive.

STOP-START CIRCUITS

OBJECTIVES

Purpose: To design and connect stop-start pushbutton circuits used to control full-voltage starters.

After completion of this project, you should be able to:
- Understand full voltage IEC and NEMA rated starters.
- Develop an understanding of stop-start control circuits.
- Connect seal-in and overload relay contacts.
- Develop an understanding of the National Electrical Code (NEC) Article 430, motors, motor circuits and controllers.

REFERENCE READING

For further information, refer to the following publications:
Industrial Control Catalog: Motor Starters, Overload Heaters and Pushbuttons, IEC and NEMA Standards. Publication A111. Allen-Bradley.
National Electric Code 1996: Article 430. Quincy, MA: National Fire Protection Association, 1995.

MATERIALS

24 V and 120 V AC power supply
(2) I.E.C. motor starters, with 24 V AC coils and NC/NO auxiliary contacts
(2) Stop-start pushbuttons
(1) Start pushbutton
(3) 24 V pilot lights
(1) 120 V pilot light
(3) Relays with 2 N/C and 1 N/O contacts

DISCUSSION

IEC and NEMA: The Organizations

The IEC (International Electro-Technical Commission) was formed in 1906 in an effort to centralize the standards for electrical equipment in the industrialized nations of western Europe. Its voting body consists of member nations, each having one vote on the commission. The United States is one of the voting members.

The IEC is international. Its activities have traditionally been associated with developing recommendations for certain product design parameters and laboratory test procedures. Manufacturers may test and publish technical information that provides customers with a basis for product comparison at a given rating. IEC standards came to reflect the needs and philosophies of western European nations. As a result, U.S. manufacturers formed the National Electrical Manufacturers Association (NEMA) in 1926.

NEMA develops design standards and test specifications to establish standardization within the North American electrical industry.

Design Philosophies

A common misconception is that the IEC and NEMA standards are very dissimilar since the designs are so different. In fact, the designs are more a reflection of the economic and political environments in which they were formed. Both designs respond to the needs of their respective markets using different underlying philosophies.

NEMA starters are designed for their ease of selection and suitability over a wide range of applications. The NEMA standards are basically *selection standards.* Manufacturers design their equipment to be selected according to a system of sizes. With NEMA starters, a size one has the same degree of rating for any suitable application regardless of manufacturer. The NEMA designs have a high level of performance over a broad range of applications. This approach has resulted in products which have a large reserve capacity, therefore larger in physical size.

The IEC standards are basically *performance standards* because the starters must pass certain performance requirements to be given a rating. With IEC starters, the selection is based much more closely on the application and duty category. When selecting an IEC starter, you must give consideration to the specific load, utilization category and required electrical life of the application. Categories AC3 and AC4 are the most relevant in selecting IEC starters for standard industrial motors. Manufacturers test their starters against these categories in order to claim a specific rating or contact life. The difference is that NEMA starters are made to be selected according to a system of sizes. With IEC starters the selection is based on utilization categories and life–load curves. Both NEMA and IEC products can be selected to provide superior performance in a wide variety of applications. Both should be selected carefully to ensure proper performance.

Overload Protection

Overload protection is an integral part of the starter which protects the motor from excessive currents. The overload relays normally supplied with IEC-rated starters provide Class 10 protection and are designed to trip within ten seconds at six times the full load current. These overload relays use an integral heater element; therefore additional heater elements are not required. To add flexibility, IEC overloads use a slide bar adjustment to adjust the proper overload trip setting for different full load current ratings depending on the motor ratings.

NEMA-rated starters require additional heater elements for their overload relays. These heaters are designated by a class number indicating the maximum time in seconds at which it will trip when carrying a current equal to 600 percent of its current rating.

A Class 10 overload relay will trip in ten seconds or less at a current equal to 600 percent of its rating. Class 10 is recommended for motors with short locked rotor time capability such as submersible pumps.

A Class 20 overload relay will trip in twenty seconds or less at a current equal to 600 percent of its rating. Class 20 is recommended for general applications.

A Class 30 overload relay will trip in thirty seconds or less at a current equal to 600 percent of its rating. Class 30 is recommended with motors driving high inertia loads where additional accelerating time is needed.

Ladder Diagram

The basic means of communicating the language of control is through the use of the ladder diagam (or line diagram) and a wiring diagram. The ladder diagram is intended to show only the circuitry which is necessary for the basic operation of the control circuit. It is not intended to show the physical relationship of the various devices in the control circuit. Rather, it leans toward simplicity, emphasizing only the electrical operation of the control circuit. See figure 1.1.

The ladder diagram consists of basically two parts: (1) The power source shown by two heavier parallel vertical lines and (2) current flow through the various parts of the circuit, such as pushbuttons, limits, contacts, coils, and overload contacts. This is shown by horizontal lines interconnecting between the power lines.

A wiring diagram includes all of the devices in the system and shows the physical relationship between these devices. The connections between the motor starter, its contacts and the pushbuttons are shown exactly as they appear on the diagram. See figure 1.2.

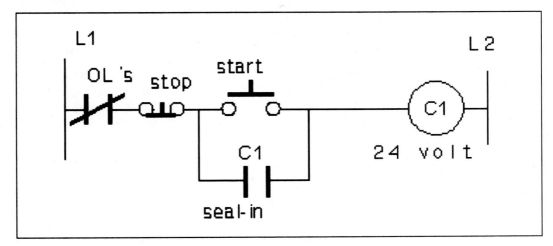

Figure 1.1. Stop-Start Ladder Diagram.

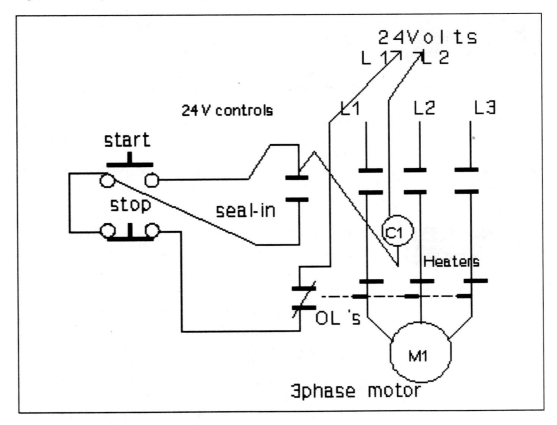

Figure 1.2. Stop-Start Wiring Diagram.

Stop-Start Push Button

Figure 1.1 shows the operation of a stop-start pushbutton. Observe the logical operations of a stop-start circuit. The normally closed stop button is connected in series with the power line. When pushed, the stop breaks the circuit causing the coil to deenergize. The normally open start button is also connected in series with the power line (logically anded with the stop button). When pushed, the start completes the circuit to energize the coil. The overloads are also connected in series with the line. This creates a three input logical and operation with the stop and starts pushbuttons. The seal-in contacts are connected in parallel with the start button (logical or operation with the start button). When the coil is energized, the seal-in contacts will close to maintain the circuit.

The project and experiments used in this project will demonstrate logic concepts and techniques that can be used with other projects in this manual.

Safety: Safety should be your primary concern. The use of safe working habits require no extra steps, but it does require common sense, proper use of equipment and adherence to electrical code and safety rules. Check with your instructor for the proper safety requirements of your lab and equipment.

Apply the following safety procedures to all projects in this book:
1. Do not work with live power. Make sure the power is disconnected when working on lab projects and experiments.
2. Use low voltage controls (30 volts or less) whenever possible.
3. Have your instructor present when the power needs to be energized to test a project or experiment.

PROGRAM LOGIC

1. A normally closed momentary stop pushbutton. When pressed, circuit will be false and motor will stop.
2. A normally opened momentary start pushbutton. When pressed, circuit will be true and motor will start.
3. A real world seal-in from the motor starter, identified as a normally open contact.
4. An IEC full voltage motor contactor with a 24 V coil, either AC or DC. A thermal overload relay selected for the appropriate current range of the motor.
5. Pressing the start button starts and seals in the motor until the stop button is depressed to stop motor.

PROCEDURES

1. Connect the control circuit for the stop-start circuit as shown in the ladder and wiring diagram described in figures 1.1 and 1.2.

   Note: Connecting a motor is not necessary for these projects and experiments, but will depend on your instructor. The objective is to become familiar with control circuit techniques.

2. Observe the first pushbutton (stop). This is normally a closed contact and should be connected in series with the line. When this button is pressed, the circuit should be open and power flow disconnected from the circuit.
3. Notice the next pushbutton (start). This is normally an open contact and should also be connected in series with the line (anded with the stop button). When pressed, this button should complete the circuit to the coil.

4. Another technique used in this project, is the real world seal-in contacts of the starter (memory contacts of starter). These contacts are connected in parallel with the start pushbutton. The seal-in contact closes when the start button is depressed and the coil is energized. It remains closed to maintain (seal-in) the coil even after the momentary start button is released.

5. The overload contacts are another important aspect of the control circuit. These normally closed contacts will open to protect the motor in case of an overload. Overload contacts should be connected in series with the coil (anded with the stop and start pushbutton).

6. Once you have completed the above procedures, test your program. With an instructor present, run your program with the motor starter only. Check the overloads and stop circuit. If it works properly, have your project checked by your instructor.

REVIEW

Now that you have successfully completed the first part of Project 1, test your understanding of the concepts covered in this project by completing the following experiments. Each experiment requires you to draw a ladder diagram before attempting to connect the circuit.

TWO-MOTOR STARTERS

Name _____   Date _____

Approved by _____

Purpose

This experiment requires you to modify Project 1 with the following:

1. Draw a ladder diagram and connect a second motor starter to your existing Project 1 (I.E.C., 24 volt, AC starter).
2. Use the same stop-start pushbutton control circuit of Project 1 to control both starters.
3. If either starter opens its overload or seal-in contacts, it will stop both starters.

Ladder Diagram

Questions

1. Determine the catalog number of I.E.C. contactors and overload relays (open type) for the following three-phase 1800 RPM, AC motors. Select contactors with 24 volt coils. Use a manufacturer's catalog. EX: Allen-Bradley bulletin 100, I.E.C. Contractors.

	Contactors	**Overloads**
A. 460 V, 7.5 hp, 11 A F.L.C. DC coil		
B. 230 V, 5 hp, 15.2 A F.L.C. AC coil		
C. 575 V, 25 hp, 27 A F.L.C. DC coil		
D. 230 V, 3 hp, 9.6 A F.L.C. AC coil		
E. 460 V, 15 hp, 21 A F.L.C. AC coil		

2. Determine the catalog number of IEC full-voltage starters (metal enclosed type enclosure) for the following three-phase, AC motors. Select starters with 24 volt AC coils and contol circuit transformer. Use a manufacturer's catalog. EX: Allen-Bradley bulletin 109, IEC Starters.

	Catalog Number
A. 460 V, 7.5 hp, 11 A F.L.C.	
B. 460 V, 15 hp, 21 A F.L.C.	
C. 575 V, 25 hp, 27 A F.L.C.	

EXPERIMENT 1.2	**TWO-STOP STARTS**

Name _____ Date _____

Approved by _____

Purpose

This experiment requires you to modify Experiment 1.1 to include the following:

1. Draw a ladder diagram and connect a second normally closed stop button and a normally open start button. This will allow you to stop and start the two motor starters from two separate locations.

2. Add a pilot light located at each pushbutton station. Pilots would be ON when motor starters are ON. The pilot will operate with same voltage as the starters.

Ladder Diagram

Questions

1. Describe the intent of the National Electrical Code article 430–6, (a).

2. Describe the intent of the NEC article 430–73, second paragraph.

EXPERIMENT 1.3	SEQUENCE START

Name _____   Date _____

Approved by _____

Purpose

This experiment requires you to design and modify Experiment 1.2 to include the following:

1. Draw a ladder diagram and reconnect each starter to its own stop-start pushbutton control circuit with pilot.
2. The second motor starter will not be able to start without starting the first motor starter.
3. Add a master emergency stop (E-Stop), push-pull button. Pushing will break the circuit. To restart, button has to be pulled back (reset).
4. Connect a pilot light to indicate when the first motor starter is OFF (light ON when starter OFF). Connect this pilot light on 120 volts.

Ladder Diagram

Question

1. Find the full voltage starters (NEMA 1) and heater size for the following motors. Use a manufacturer's catalog. EX: Allen-Bradley bulletin 509, Full-Voltage Starters with 120 V Coil and Control Circuit Transformer.

			HEATERS		
Motors		Starter Size	Class 10	20	30
A.	5 hp, 460 V, 7.6 amp F.L.C.	_____	___	___	___
B.	7 1/2 hp, 230 V, 22 amp F.L.C.	_____	___	___	___
C.	15 hp, 230 V, 42 amp F.L.C.	_____	___	___	___
D.	20 hp, 575 V, 22 amp F.L.C.	_____	___	___	___
E.	30 hp, 460 V, 40 amp F.L.C.	_____	___	___	___
F.	60 hp, 575 V, 62 amp F.L.C.	_____	___	___	___
G.	100 hp, 575 V, 99 amp F.L.C.	_____	___	___	___

EXPERIMENT
1.4

SINGLE PUSHBUTTON SEQUENCE

Name _____   Date _____

Approved by _____

Purpose

Connect the circuit diagram shown below in figure 1.3 using the following:
1. A single normally closed/normally open pushbutton to start the two motor starters in sequence (a delay between the start of each motor starter). Pressing the start button would energize motor starter #1. Releasing the same start would start motor starter #2.
2. Use two low voltage control full voltage starters.
3. Use a single stop pushbutton to stop motors. Any overload contact tripping will stop both motors.

Ladder Diagram

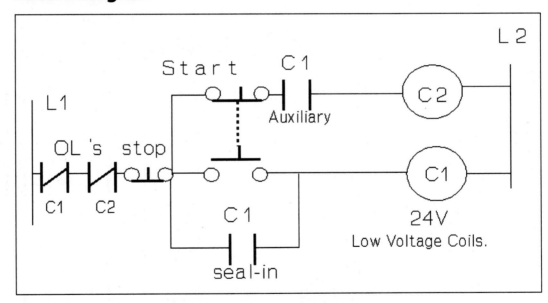

Figure 1.3. Single Pushbutton Sequence.

Question

1. Select a standard duty stop-start/pilot pushbutton station from an industrial control catalog. EX: A-B bulletin 800S, Standard Duty, NEMA 1.

NON-SEQUENTIAL LIGHTS

Name _____ Date _____

Approved by _____

Purpose

Connect the circuit diagram shown below in figure 1.4 using the following:
1. Three low voltage relays with two N/O contacts and two N/C contacts.
2. Three momentary start buttons, each to control a low voltage relay. The relays to control a light output. Only one light can be sealed ON once a button has been pressed. When more than one button is pressed, the corresponding lights will be turned ON.

Ladder Diagram

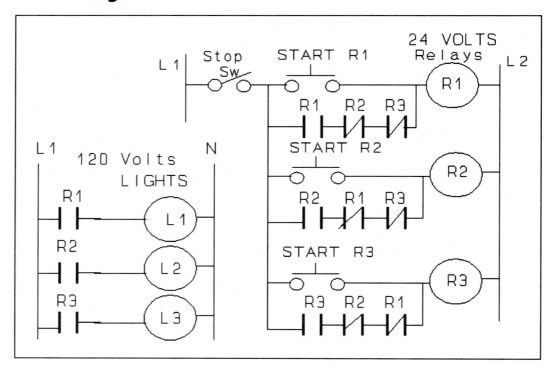

Figure 1.4. Low Voltage Relay Controlling Lights.

Question

1. Using a manufacturer's industrial control catalog, select a relay that could be used to control the lights in this experiment.

Type and Catalog No. _____

RUN-JOG CIRCUITS

OBJECTIVES

Purpose: To design and connect stop–start and jog pushbutton circuits using selector and roto–push switches.

After completion of this project, you should be able to:
- Design and connect stop–start jog circuits.
- Investigate and connect roto–push units (roto-push selector switches).

REFERENCE READING

To preview the switches that are used in this project, refer to Appendix B: Roto–Push Units® and Contact Block Components.

For futher information, refer to the following publication:
Industrial Control Catalog: Roto–Push® Units and Selector Switches. Publication DU-100. Cutler Hammer Products.

MATERIALS

24 V and 120 V power supply
(1) I.E.C. motor starter with 24 V AC coil
(1) Three position roto–push selector switch (C–H 10250 T261–7)
(1) Contact block (10250–T1)
(1) Stop–run/jog pushbutton

DISCUSSION

Jogging

Jogging or inching are terms that describe the frequent starting and stopping of a motor for short periods of time. Jogging is used to position materials by moving the material small distances each time the jog button is depressed. When connecting a jogging circuit the seal–in contacts must be isolated (disconnected) from the circuit. There are various methods to accomplish this: (1) A selector switch (two-position) can be used to manually open or close a portion (seal–in) of the electrical circuit. This is called selector run/jog. (2) A separate momentary pushbutton to energize a relay coil. The relay contacts can be used as seal–in contacts for the run circuit. The jog pushbutton would energize the starter, without the seal–in contacts. This is called relay run/jog. (3) Roto–push selector pushbutton provide the combined functions of the above pushbutton and selector switch. This is called roto–push run/jog. All of these circuits will be explored in this project.

Roto–Push Units

Roto–push units (roto-push selector switches) provide two, and three control functions that can be obtained in the space normally required by a single pushbutton element. The outer collar can be turned to two or three positions to make or break control circuits. The circuits can then be completed by pressing the same pushbutton in any one of the positions.

The following steps can be used to properly select roto–push buttons:

1. The first step in selecting the proper button is to design the electrical circuit following the methods you would normally use in designing circuitry with standard ladder diagrams. This circuit is similar to a basic stop–start button, shown in figure 1.1. The only difference in this project is the seal–in contacts need to be disconnected from the circuit in the jog position. When designing circuits with roto–push switches, it is more suitable to identify the switch operation using a function table. Set up the logic of the circuit using open contact spaces and identify them with any label. See the diagram in figure 2.1a. The open spaces are labeled J and K.

2. Once you complete the design of your circuit, the next step is to develop a function table of your circuit. A function table is a means of signifying the complete logic operations of the circuit. To design the function table, logically place the operating functions of the contacts in an organized table. Use X or 1 to denote a depress or close position (D). Use O to denote an open or normal position (N).

   A normally open start button would be O, X. The free or open position is O and the depressed or closed position is X. A normally closed stop button would be X, O. Any other situation would be a combination of X, X, or O, O.

   Keep in mind that all logic operations need to be identified for each position of the roto-push selector switch. The same pushbutton could have three different logic operations. See the function table of figure 2.1 (b). The top line identifies the free or normal (N) and depress (D) of each position.

3. The next step is to compare your function table with the circuit sequences of the manufacturer to select a matching combination. In the table for example, we are comparing the functions with Table 2a, Cam and Contact Block for Three Position Switches in Appendix B. Combination number 11 matches our top horizontal line of the function table (OX–OO–OX). Combination number 26 matches the bottom line of our function table (XX–OO–OO). Mark these numbers down in your function table. The next step is to find a common cam that can operate those two combinations.

4. Scan the row to the right of the combinations you have selected for a contact symbol. If a contact symbol is shown, the cam listed at the top will perform the logic operation of that combination. The cam that you select must be capable of operating all the combinations of your function table. The cam selected for this circuit is cam number 7. The next step is to select an operator with the identified Cam 7. The part number for this operation would be C–H 10250T261–7. This would provide a three position operator (black long) with cam 7. See Table Operator and Cam, Appendix B.

5. At this point, we need to order the contacts for the operator and cam. To select the contacts, check Table 2a in Appendix B. Look at your selected combinations. Combination 11 requires a normally open contact. Combination 26 requires a normally close contact.

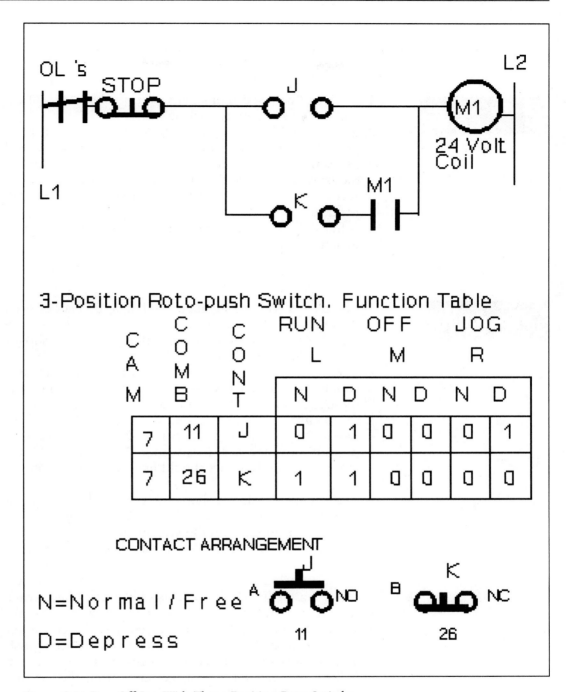

3-Position Roto-push Switch. Function Table

CAM	COMB	CONT	RUN L		OFF M		JOG R	
			N	D	N	D	N	D
7	11	J	0	1	0	0	0	1
7	26	K	1	1	0	0	0	0

CONTACT ARRANGEMENT

N=Normal/Free

D=Depress

Figure 2.1. Run-Off-Jog With Three-Position Roto Switch.

Letters A and B represent the locations occupied by the two circuits of the contact block in relation to the locating nib of the operator. The nib is situated in the front part of the operator. For proper operation, all the A contacts should be lined up with the nib. See Table of Contact Block Components, Appendix B. The unit for this project requires a 10250-1, NC/NO contact block. Assemble the complete unit and verify its operation with a continuity meter. Check the operation of the contacts. The switch should function exactly as your function table.

The project and experiments used in this project will demonstrate logic concepts and techniques that can be used with other projects in this manual.

1. A normally closed momentary stop pushbutton. When pressed, the circuit will be false and motor will stop.
2. A three-position roto–push selector switch. When pressed in the left position, the motor will start and continue running. When the middle is OFF, pressing the button will not activate the motor. In the right position, the motor will jog when the button is depressed.
3. A real world seal–in from the motor starter is identified as a normally open contact.
4. A full voltage motor starter with a 24 V coil and its overload contacts wired in series with the coil.

1. Complete a wiring diagram according to the ladder diagram shown in figure 2.1 of a run–off–jog pushbutton station.
2. Connect the circuit for the run–off–jog circuit as shown in your wiring diagram and described in figure 2.1.
3. Observe the first pushbutton (stop). This is a normally closed contact and it should be connected in series with the line. When this button is pressed, the circuit should be open and the power flow will be disconnected from the circuit.
4. Assemble your three-position roto–push switch. You should have a three-position operator with a cam code 7. Install a NO/NC contact block to the operator. The A contact should line up with the nib on the front facing the operator.
5. The roto–push selector should be connected according to your diagram. The normally open A contact is anded with the stop button. The normally closed B contact is anded with the seal–in contact. The function of the button is to turn the coil ON in the left position, OFF in the middle, and ON in the right position.
6. Another technique used in this project is the real world seal–in contacts of the starter (memory contacts of starter). These contacts are always connected in parallel with the start pushbutton. The seal–in contact closes when the start button is depressed and the coil is energized. In this circuit, the normally closed B contacts of the roto–push are anded (series) with the seal–in contacts. The B contacts of the roto–push selector switch will disconnect the seal–in contacts from the circuit in the jog position and in the OFF position.
7. It is important that you line up the A contacts with the nib on the collar in the front of the operator. Otherwise, the operation sequence could be reversed.
8. The overload contacts are also important aspects of the control circuit. These normally closed contacts will open to protect the motor in case of an overload. The overload contacts should be connected in series with the coil (anded with the stop and start pushbutton).
9. Once you have completed this procedure, test your circuit. With instructor present, run your circuit with motor starter only. Check the overloads and the stop circuit.

REVIEW   Now that you have successfully completed the first part of Project 2, to test your understanding of the concepts covered in this project, proceed to complete the following experiments.

Note: Connecting a motor is not necessary for the purpose of these experiments. This will depend on your instructor. The objective is to become familiar with control circuit techniques. Use low voltage controls (30 volts or less) whenever possible.

EXPERIMENT 2.1

JOG-OFF-AUTO

Name _____ Date _____

Approved by _____

Purpose

Design and draw a ladder diagram with a function table of the following parameters:

Use a three-position roto–push switch, a normally closed push–pull stop button, a momentary single pole switch used for the auto, and a motor starter with a low voltage coil. The operation of the switch: In the middle position all circuits would be turned off. In the left position, pressing the switch will jog the starter. Turning the switch to the right would activate the automatic circuit immediately. The motor starter would then operate by a single pole automatic switch.

Ladder Diagram and Function Table

Question

Design a ladder diagram with a function table of a circuit with the following operations:

- Left position = press to jog motor starter #1.
- Middle position = press to jog motor starter #2.
- Right position = press to jog motor starter #3.

RELAY JOG 1

Name _____   Date _____

Approved by _____

Purpose

Connect the relay jog circuit shown in figure 2.2 using the following parameters:
1. Use a relay with two normally open contacts along with the starter seal–in contacts are used to seal–in the run circuit.
2. Use a normally open, standard start pushbutton for the run. Pressing this button would energize the relay and the motor starter.
3. A second normally open start standard pushbutton for the jog. Pressing this button would jog the motor only. The relay would not be energized.

Ladder Diagram

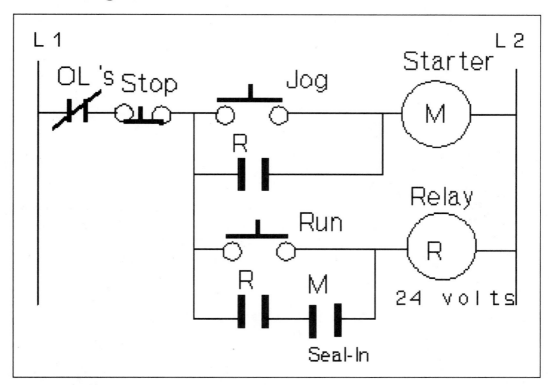

Figure 2.2. Relay Jog Using Standard Pushbuttons.

Question

Design a stop circuit using a two position roto–push switch, (stop/safestop). Show the function table and catalog number of switch. In the left position, the roto would operate as a regular stop pushbutton. In the right position, the circuit would be opened (inoperable).

<table>
<tr><td>**EXPERIMENT**
2.3</td></tr>
</table>

RELAY JOG 2

Name _____   Date _____

Approved by _____

Purpose

Modify Experiment 2.2 to operate in the following manner.
1. Pressing the jog button would jog the motor starter. This operation is the same as the sequence in Experiment 2.2.
2. Pressing the run button by itself would not start the run motor starter. In order to run the motor, both the run and the jog button need to be pressed together. (Hint: Only one connection needs to be changed from the relay jog 1 circuit in Experiment 2.2.)

Ladder Diagram

Question

Design a circuit and function table using a two-position roto–push switch to control a motor starter (run–jog). The circuit would operate in the following manner:
1. Turning to the left position and push will run the starter.
2. Turning to the right position and push will jog the starter.
3. Motor has to be stopped for jog.
4. Draw a ladder diagram and a function table.

EXPERIMENT
2.4

RELAY JOG 1

Name _____   Date _____

Approved by _____

Purpose

Design and draw a ladder diagram of a circuit using a three-position roto–push switch to control two motor starters as follows:

1. Left position and pressed would jog motor starter #1.
2. Middle position and pressed would jog motor starter #2.
3. Right position and pressed would run and seal–in motor starters #1 and #2. Motors have to be stopped to jog. Show the function table.

Ladder Diagram

Question

Design a ladder diagram and a function table for circuit that would use a three-position selector switch. (This is not a roto-push selector switch.) Use a manufacturer's industrial control catalog and select a three-position selector switch. Select a standard knob with spring return from left and right that would operate in the following:

Left = Run solenoid #1, Middle = off, Right = Run solenoid #3. Only one solenoid can be on at any one time.

FORWARD/REVERSE CIRCUITS

OBJECTIVES

Purpose: To design and connect a forward-off-reverse pushbutton circuit using a roto-push selector switch.

After completion of this project, you should be able to:
- Connect full voltage reversing starters.
- Understand and connect forward/reverse circuits.
- Connect three-position roto-switches.

REFERENCE READING

To preview the switches that are used in this project, refer to Appendix B: Roto-Push® Units and Contact Block Components.

For further information, refer to the following publication:
Industrial Control Catalog: Full Voltage Reversing Starters and Overload Heaters, I.E.C. & NEMA Standards. Publication A111. Allen-Bradley.

MATERIALS

24 V and 120 V AC power supply
(1) Forward/reverse starter (IEC, 24 V coils)
(1) Stop-forward/reverse pushbutton
(1) Three-position roto-push switch (C-H 10250 T261-8)
(2) Contact blocks (C-H 10250-T1)
(1) Contact block (C-H 10250-T3)

DISCUSSION

Reversing Starters

Many control applications require that a three-phase motor be capable of running in the forward and reverse direction. In order to accomplish this, a full-voltage starter is needed for both the forward and reverse directions (reversing starters). These reversing starters may also be used on plugging applications. Reversing starters are electrically and mechanically interlocked to keep both starters from being closed simultaneously.

Although most magnetic reversing starters provide electrical and mechanical interlocked protection, some control circuits provide a secondary safety back-up system to ensure electrical interlocking. Figure 3.1 illustrates a circuit using a three-position roto-push. This circuit uses a three-position roto-push to provide the following: (1) In the left position and pressing roto-push the motor runs in a forward direction. (2) In the middle position, the motor is OFF. This insures an electrical interlock between the forward and reverse direction. (3) Turning to the right position and pressing the roto-button starts the motor in reverse.

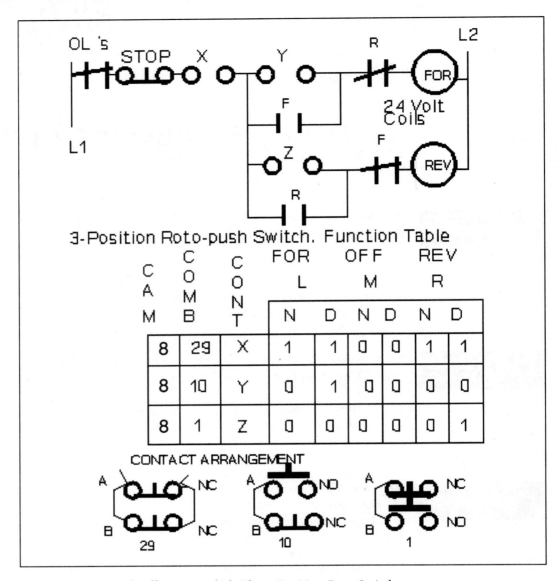

Figure 3.1. Forward-Off-Reverse With Three-Position Roto Switch.

PROGRAM LOGIC

1. A normally closed momentary stop pushbutton. When pressed, circuit will be false and motor will stop.
2. A three-position roto-pushbutton.
   Left position = forward direction
   Middle position = OFF
   Right position = reverse direction
3. A full voltage reversing starters with the following: (1) 24 V coils. (2) Normally closed auxiliary contacts for electrical interlock. (3) Normally open seal-in contacts. (4) Overload contacts.

PROCEDURES

1. Connect the starter circuit and identify the cam and contacts for the ladder diagram shown in figure 3.1. The circuit requires a three-position roto-push switch for a forward-off-reverse circuit.
2. Assemble the proper operator (cam) and contacts for the circuit. You should be using an operator with a cam 8. You should also install three NO/NC

contact blocks to the operator. The A contacts of all three contact blocks should line up with the nib on the front of the operator. Before connecting the circuit, it is always a good idea to check your equipment. Using a multimeter, verify the the contact arrangement of your switch with the function table in figure 3.1.

3. Observe the first pushbutton (stop). This is a normally closed contact and it should be connected in series with the line. When this button is pressed, the circuit should be open and power flow disconnected.

4. The roto-push selector switch should do all the work in this circuit. Turning to the left and pressing should energize the forward starter. The middle is OFF. Turning to the right and pressing should energize the reverse starter.

5. The real world seal-in contact of both the forward and reverse starters are connected the same as a start button. These contacts are always connected in parallel with the start pushbutton. The seal-in contact closes when the start button is depressed and the coil is energized. It remains closed to maintain (seal-in) the coil even after the momentary start button is released.

6. The overload contact is another important aspect of the control circuit. These normally closed contacts will open to protect the motor in case of an overload. Overload contacts should be connected in series with the coil (anded with the stop and start pushbutton).

7. On forward/reverse circuits, a set of nomally closed auxiliary contacts is always use to electrically interlock the starters.

8. Once you have completed this procedure test your circuit. With an instructor present, run your circuit with the motor starter only. Check the overloads and the stop circuit. If your control circuit operates properly, check with your instructor regarding the connection of a motor. Connecting a motor is not necessary for this project and experiments.

REVIEW

Now that you have successfully completed the first part of Project 3.0, which tests, your understanding of the concepts covered in this project, complete the following experiments. Each experiment requires you to design and draw a ladder diagram before attempting to connect the circuit.

<table>
<tr><td>**EXPERIMENT**
3.1</td><td>**STANDARD FORWARD/REVERSE**

Name _____   Date _____
Approved by _____</td></tr>
</table>

Purpose

Connect a forward/reverse circuit with the following specifications:
1. A normally closed stop pushbutton, two normally open start pushbuttons. One forward/reverse starter.
2. One start button is used for the forward and one for the reverse.
3. Pressing either the forward or reverse buttons would start the motor in either forward or reverse. To start in the opposite direction when in run mode, the motor has to be stopped.

Ladder Diagram

Questions

1. What is the purpose of the electrical interlocks in a forward/reverse starter?

2. Determine the catalog number of IEC forward/reverse contactors and overload relays for the following 3-phase AC motors. Select contactors with 24 volt AC coils (enclosed type). EX: A-B bulletin 105, IEC Reversing Starters.

A. 460 V, 5 hp, 7.6 A F.L.C. _____

B. 460 V, 10 hp, 14 A F.L.C. _____

C. 460 V, 15 hp, 21 A F.L.C. _____

D. 575 V, 30 hp, 32 A F.L.C. _____

EXPERIMENT 3.2

REV JOG-FOR RUN-REV JOG

Name _____   Date _____

Approved by _____

Purpose

Design a ladder diagram and a function table for controlling forward/reverse motor starters #1 and #2 with the following specifications:

1. One three-position roto push selector switch, one master stop pushbutton, two forward/reverse starters.
2. In order to go from run to jog, the circuit has to be stopped. Either of the starters tripping an overload will stop both motors.
3. Select the roto-switch switch necessary to perform the operation below.
   Left position = press, for jog of reverse starter #1.
   Middle postion = press, for run of forward starters #1 & #2.
   Right position = press, for jog of reverse starter #2.

Ladder Diagram

Question

1. From a manufacturer's catalog, find the full-voltage forward/reverse starters (NEMA 1) and heater size for the following motors: EX: Allen-Bradley bulletin 505, Full-Voltage Reversing Starters with 120 V Coils. Ambient temperature same at controller and motor.

	Size	Cat Number	Class 10	20
A. 5 hp, 230 V, 15.2 A F.L.C.	_____	_____	_____	____
B. 7$\frac{1}{2}$ hp, 460 V, 11 A F.L.C.	_____	_____	_____	____
C. 15 hp, 460 V, 21 A F.L.C.	_____	_____	_____	____
D. 20 hp, 460 V, 27 A F.L.C.	_____	_____	_____	____
E. 30 hp, 575 V, 32 A F.L.C.	_____	_____	_____	____

FORWARD RUN-4 STARTERS

Name _____   Date _____

Approved by _____

Purpose

Design a function table and draw a ladder diagram of a circuit with the following specifications:

1. Use a three-position roto-push switch. Select the switch from a manufacturers catalog. One master stop pushbutton, three operating motor starters #1, #2, #3 with NC auxiliary contacts and one lubricating pump motor starter #4.
2. Select a three-position roto-push switch with the following operation:
   Left position = press starts #4 and #3.
   Middle position = press starts #4 and #2.
   Right position = press starts #4 and #1.
   Interlock the positions to operate only one position at a time.

Ladder Diagram

Question

1. From a manufacturer's catalog, find the combination reversing starters (NEMA 4) and heater size for the following motors EX: Allen-Bradley bulletin 507, Combination Reversing Starter with a Circuit Breaker and 120 V Coil:

	Size	Catalog Number	Overloads Class 20
A. 1 hp, 230 V, 3.6 A F.L.C.	_____	_____	_____
B. 3 hp, 230 V, 9.6 A F.L.C.	_____	_____	_____
C. 5 hp, 230 V, 15.2 A F.L.C.	_____	_____	_____
D. 10 hp, 230 V, 28 A F.L.C.	_____	_____	_____

TIMING CIRCUITS

Purpose: To connect two timer–off delays with a forward/reverse circuit.

After completion of this project, you should be able to:
- Read and interpret ladder diagrams with timers.
- Design and connect time delay logic circuits.
- Select timer–on delay and timer–off delay timers.
- Understand and connect PLC I/O module circuits.

For further information, refer to the following publications:
Industrial Control Catalog: Timing Relays, IEC and NEMA Standards. Publication A111. Allen-Bradley.
PLC-5 Family Programmable Controllers: Hardware Installation Manual. Publication 1785-6.6.1. Allen-Bradley.

24 V and 120 V power supply
(1) Forward/reverse starter
(1) Stop–forward/reverse pushbutton
(2) OFF–delay timers
(2) ON–delay timers

Timers

Timing relays can be supplied to provide the time delay in either of two ways. The first arrrangement, on–delay, provides the time delay after the coil is energized. The second arrangement, off–delay, provides the time delay after the coil is deenergized.

Timer on–delay schematic symbols are shown in figure 4.1.a. When power is applied to the coil TR, a preset period of time passes before the contacts change state. When the power is removed from the coil, the contacts instantly revert back to their original position. Figure 4.1.b shows a timer–on delay (TON) circuit. When the start pushbutton operating the T1 coil is closed, the rung is made true and a timing action begins. After an accumulation of nine seconds, the normally open timing contact will close to operate the light. When the stop pushbutton is open, allowing the rung to go false, an instant action will cause the timing contacts to return instantly to their normal position.

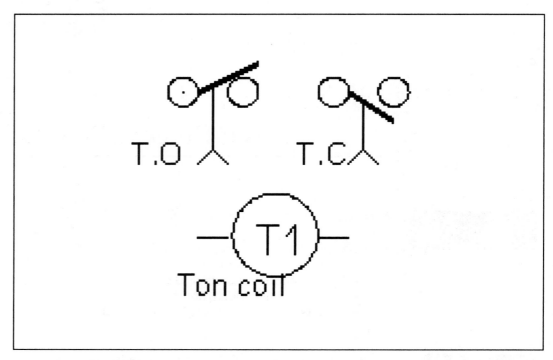

Figure 4.1a. Ton Symbols.

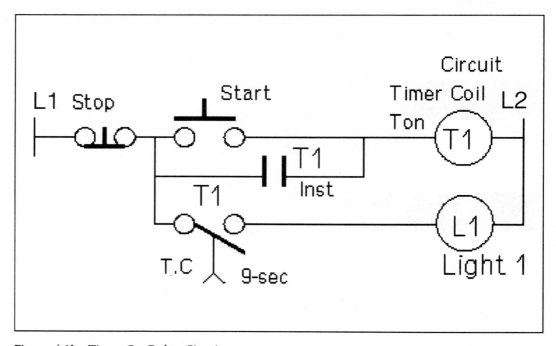

Figure 4.1b. Timer On-Delay Circuit.

Timer off–delay schematic symbols are shown in figure 4.2.a. When voltage is applied to the coil, the contacts change state immediately. The timing contacts remain in their opposite state as long as power is applied to the coil. When the power is removed from the coil, the contacts return to their normal state only after a preset time period.

The second circuit (see figure 4.2.b) is a timer–off delay (TOF) circuit. When the start push button operating the T2 coil is closed and the rung is true, an instant action occurs. This causes the timing contacts to close instantly and turn the light on. When the stop pushbutton is open, making the rung false, the timing action begins. After an accumulation of nine seconds, the normally open timing contacts will open to turn off the light.

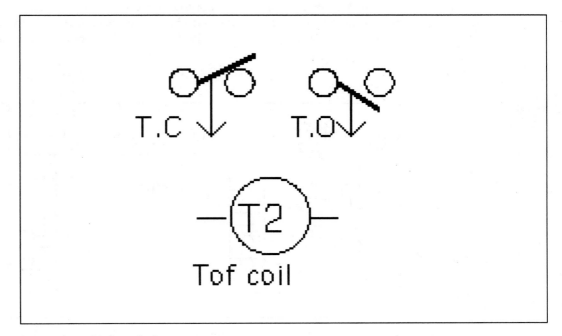

Figure 4.2a. Tof Symbols.

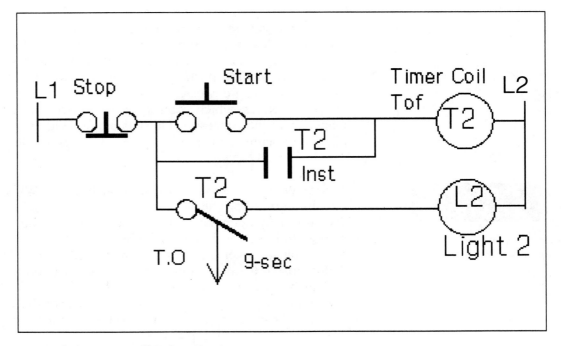

Figure 4.2b. Timer Off-Delay Circuit.

PLC Input/Output Modules

A programmable logic controller (PLC) is a solid state logic control device for industrial applications. As the term *programmable* indicates, the controller has an essential difference from hardwired controls. Its logic function is determined by a user entered program, which specifies how output devices operate in response to input devices. Because the program is stored in a read and write memory, a change in a controlled process is accomplished by reprogramming rather than by extensive rewiring, as hardwired control systems require. The controller continuously monitors the status of devices connected as inputs. Based on user program instruction, the controller then controls the devices connected as outputs. See figure 4.3 I/O connections.

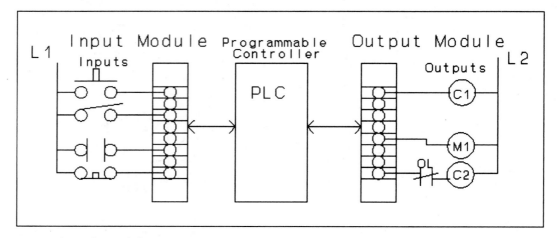

Figure 4.3. I/0 Module Connections.

There are two general I/O module types:
1. Input modules, which sense the voltage levels of input devices and provide the processor with the logic level status information on these devices. Inputs may include pushbuttons, selector switches, limits and other sensing and switching devices.
2. Output modules, which control output devices, based on logic level commands from the processor. Outputs may include various types of full–voltage motor starters, solenoids, alarms, displays and indicator lights

PROGRAM LOGIC

1. A normally closed momentary stop pushbutton. When pressed, circuit will be false and motor will stop.
2. Two normally open start pushbuttons. One start button for the forward direction and one for the reverse direction.
3. A full voltage reversing starter with the following: (1) 24 V coils. (2) Normally closed auxiliary contacts for electrical interlock. (3) Normally open seal–in contacts. (4) Overload contacts.
4. Two timer off–delay relays. One for the forward and one for the reverse starters. These are separate timing relays or time delay contact blocks that snap on to individual starters.

5. The circuit operates as a standard forward/reverse circuit. See Project 3, Experiment 3.1. The difference is,; the addition of two timer–off delays that will prevent the motor from being started in the opposite direction too quickly after a stop.

PROCEDURES

1. Connect the circuit for the forward/reverse circuit as shown in the ladder diagram described in figure 4.4.

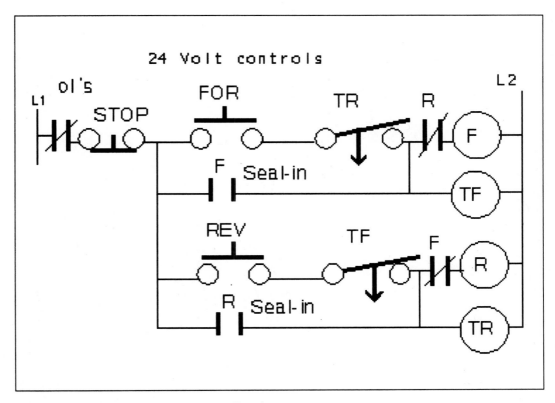

Figure 4.4. Forward/Reverse Timer Off-Delay.

2. This circuit requires two timer off–delay relays. One timer coil is wired in parallel with the forward starter coil, the other is wired in parallel with the reverse starter. Each timer uses a normally closed, time close contact to interlock the forward and reverse starters.
3. Observe the timer contacts. These are normally closed, time close contacts. When the forward timer coil (TF) is energized, its associated timing contact (TF) connected in series with the reverse coil will instantly open and time close. This will prevent the reverse coil from being energized for a period of time after the forward coil is deenergized. The opposite situation applies to the reverse coil. When the reverse coil is energized, the forward coil will be interlocked from starting for a period of time.

4. Once you have completed this procedure, proceed to test your program. With an instructor present, run your program with motor starter only. Check the overloads and the stop circuit. If it works properly, have the project checked by your instructor.

REVIEW   Now that you have successfully completed the first part of Project 4, to test your understanding of the concepts covered in this project, proceed to complete the following experiments. Each experiment requires you to draw a ladder diagram before attempting to connect the circuit.

EXPERIMENT 4.1

TIMED SEQUENCE STARTS 1

Name _____   Date _____

Approved by _____

Purpose

Design and connect a control circuit that will sequence start three motor starters. The circuit operation is as follows:

1. Use a momentary start pushbutton to start the sequence. A push–pull stop button for emergency stopping and a momentary stop as the standard operation stop. Two timer–on delay timers and three motor starters with low voltage 24 volt, AC coils are needed.

2. Motor starter #1 would start first by pressing the start button. Ten seconds later, motor starter #2 would start, by timer one. Ten more seconds and motor starter #3 would start, by the second timer. Pressing either stop pushbuttons would stop all three motor starters.

Ladder Diagram

Questions

1. Using an industrial control catalog, select two ON delay timers that would satisfy the requirements of the above experiment. EX: Allen–Bradley bulletin 700 type N, Industrial Relay with Pneumatic Timer.

2. Using an industrial control catalog, select the I.E.C. contactor and overload relay needed for the previous experiment. Use the timer accessories added to the contactors. (The motors are 5 hp, 460 V, 7.6 A F.L.C.). Identify type and catalog numbers.

EXPERIMENT 4.2

TIMED SEQUENCE STARTS 2

Name _____   Date _____

Approved by _____

Purpose

Design a ladder diagram circuit and modify the circuit in Experiment 4.1 to include the following:

1. The start sequence would remain the same as Experiment 4.1.
2. The difference would be in the stop sequence. Pressing the momentary standard stop would stop motor starter #2 and #3 immediately. Motor starter #1 would remain running for five seconds longer (TOF) before stopping.
3. Pressing the E–Stop completely turns everything OFF.

This circuit utilizes two timer–on and one timer–off delay timers.

Ladder Diagram

Question

1. Using an industrial control catalog, select a timer–off delay (TOF) timer that would satisfy the requirements of the above experiment. EX: Allen–Bradley bulletin 700 type N, Industrial relay with Pneumatic Timer.

EXPERIMENT 4.3	Name _____ Date _____
	Approved by _____

TIMED PRESS UNIT

Purpose

Connect the timing circuit shown below in figure 4.5 with the following:
1. Two momentary start pushbuttons to control a solenoid (SO).
2. Both pushbuttons have to be pressed simultaneously within a preset time (0.1 to 10 second range). If they are not both pressed within the preset time of both T1 and T2 timers, the solenoid will not be activated.

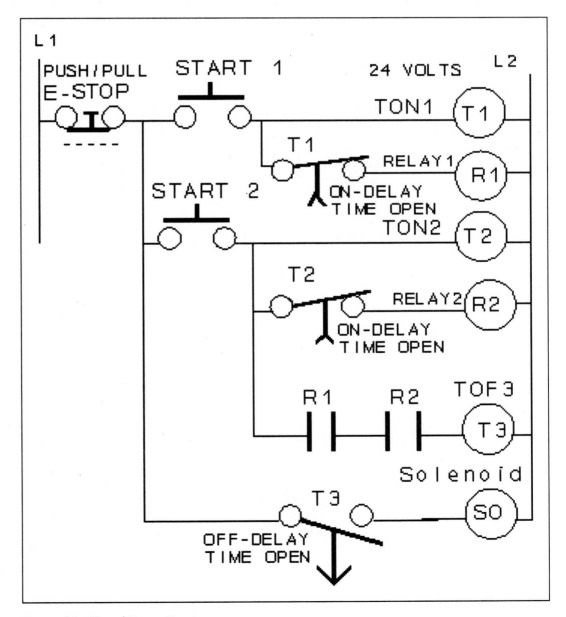

Figure 4.5. Timed Press Circuit.

3. When activated, the solenoid would operate for a set time and then drop out (1 to 180 second range).

4. This circuit utilizes two timer–on delays and one timer–off delay, 24 V AC.

    Note: It is important to use a push–pull maintained stop button. Pushing the stop will open and maintain an open circuit. To restart, the stop has to be pulled to release. (EX: A–B, 800T–FX6D4).

Ladder Diagram

Question

1. Using an industrial control catalog, select two on-delay and one off–delay timers that would satisfy the requirements of the previous experiment. (EX: Allen–Bradley bulletin 700 type HT, Single Range Plug–In, 24 V AC Timing Relays.

TIMED SWITCH CIRCUIT

Name _____   Date _____

Approved by _____

Purpose

Connect the circuit shown in figure 4.6. After you have connected the the circuit, perform the following:
1. Turn the selector switch ON and immediately turn it OFF. The circuit should remain ON for the preset time of the timer–on delay.
2. Turn the selector switch immediately ON after the circuit deenergizes. The circuit should remain OFF for a preset time of the timer–off delay.
3. This circuit is designed to control the ON/OFF time of the switch and prevent false starts.

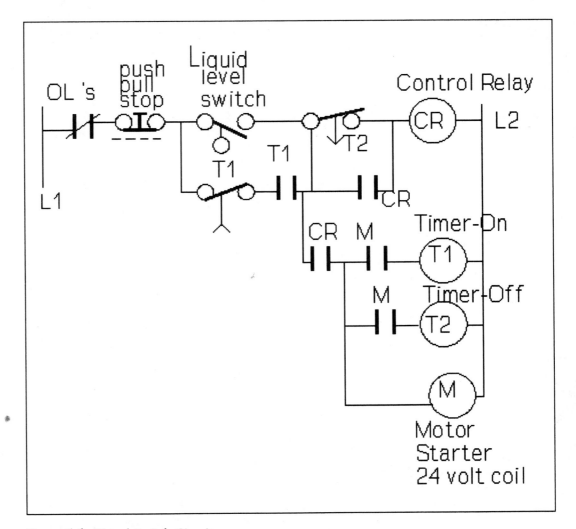

Figure 4.6. Timed Switch Circuit.

Ladder Diagram

Question

1. Using an industrial control catalog, select a solid state ON delay timer that would satisfy the requirements of the above experiment. (EX: Allen–Bradley bulletin 700 type, PS Timer with a Type P Relay).

<table>
<tr><td>**EXPERIMENT**
4.5</td><td colspan="2">**TWO SPEED COMPELLING CIRCUIT**</td></tr>
</table>

EXPERIMENT 4.5

TWO SPEED COMPELLING CIRCUIT

Name _____   Date _____

Approved by _____

Purpose

This experiment is a design problem only. Design a ladder diagram for a three–phase, two speed, constant horsepower motor. See motor connection figure 4.7. The circuit is to operate as follows:

1. The circuit calls for a three-position roto–push switch.
2. The operator can select the desired speed by pressing either the low or high pushbutton.
3. By pressing the low pushbutton, the motor will start and run in low. Pressing the high pushbutton, the motor will start in low and then run in high speed after a preset time (1.5 to 30 seconds).
4. The operator is required to press the stop pushbutton before changing speed from high to low.

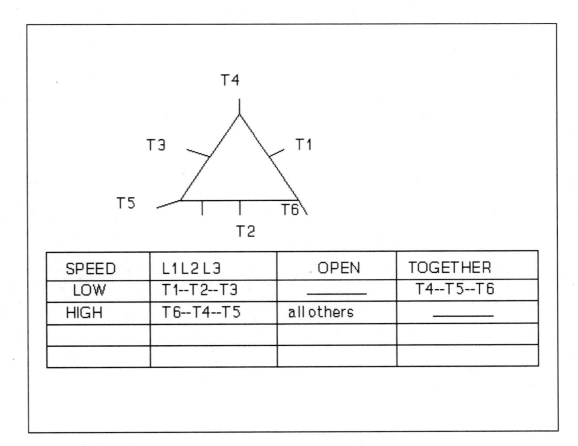

SPEED	L1 L2 L3	OPEN	TOGETHER
LOW	T1--T2--T3	_____	T4--T5--T6
HIGH	T6--T4--T5	all others	_____

Figure 4.7. 2-Speed Constant Horsepower Motor Connection.

Ladder Diagram

Questions

1. Using the hardware layout of your PLC installation manual, show the connection diagram for the coil of a low voltage motor stater connected to a low voltage output module.
2. Using the hardware layout of your PLC installation manual, show the connection diagram for the normally open contact (seal–in) of a starter connected to a low voltage input module. Also connect a normally closed stop, a normally open start pushbutton, and normally closed auxiliary contact to the same input module.

AC DRIVE SYSTEM

OBJECTIVES

Purpose: To investigate speed control of a three-phase motor using an adjustable frequency AC motor drive.

After completion of this project, you should be able to:
- Configure the initial settings of the AC drive.
- Program the various parameters of an AC drive for speed control of a three–phase motor.
- Investigate the operating functions of an AC drive.

REFERENCE READING

For further information, refer to the following publications:
Adjustable Frequency AC Drive: Programming Manual, Bulletin 1336. Publication 1336-5.1. Allen-Bradley.
Adjustable Frequency AC Drive: Hardware User Manual, Bulletin 1336. Publication 1336-5.0. Allen-Bradley.

MATERIALS

(1) Adjustable frequency drive, 1336–B003–EAD–FA2–L2 or equivelant
(1) Stop–start and jog pushbutton
(1) Reverse switch
(1) Two-position speed selector switch

DISCUSSION

An AC adjustable frequency drive typically consists of two basic control functions: operator controls and programming parameters. The operator controls allow the operator to start, stop, auto/manual, and change direction and speed of the controller by simply turning potentiometers or other operator devices. The drive may be operated locally from a front mounted control panel or through an interface board using external control devices. See figure 5.1 interface board connections. The programming parameters may be programmed locally from a front mounted control panel or through the serial communications port using optional devices. Four pushbuttons on the local display and programming panel are used for both viewing and programming parameters. Parameters may be viewed while the drive is running, but not changed. A decimal displayed in the far right corner indicates the programming mode. See figure 5.2 display panel.

The PR pushbutton is used to switch from the operating display to the parameter viewing display. Once in the viewing display, the pushbutton is used to increment through the parameters. The ENTER pushbutton is used to switch from viewing to programming only when the parameter 0 is displayed. The ENTER is also used to store the displayed values. The INCREMENT and DECREMENT pushbuttons are used to scroll up or down to the parameter value to be entered. Pressing both buttons simultaneously will end programming.

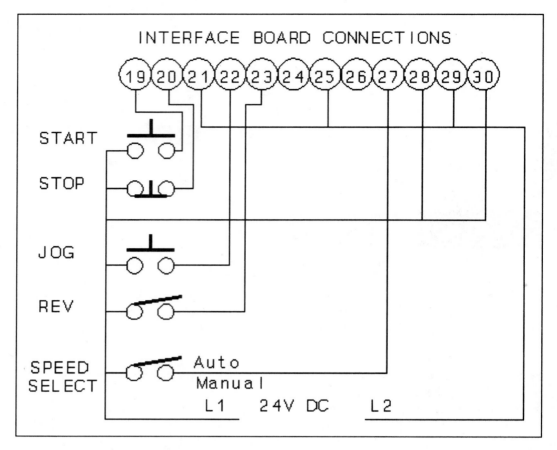

Figure 5.1. Interface Board Connections.

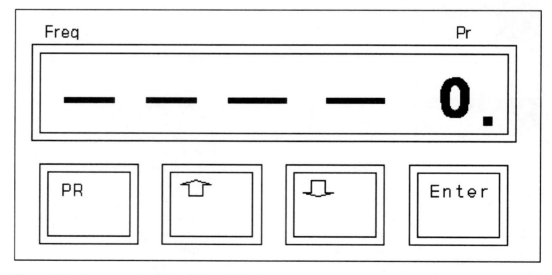

Figure 5.2. Programming Panel For AC Drive.

Project

This project is designed to familiarize you with some of the terminology and parameters by which an AC drive is programmed. Each control function has its own parameter which is a part of the overall program to operate the AC drive. The AB 1336 drive is used as the means to program these parameters.

It is important to maintain good notes on this project. The information from this project will be utilized later on Project 20, Digital to Analog.

PROGRAM LOGIC

1. Follow all the drive wiring and safety guidelines listed in the manufacturer's manual.
2. Connect the operator remote control pushbuttons (stop–start–jog, reverse and selector sw) to the interface board.

PROCEDURES

1. Check with your instructor to assure that all necessary steps have been taken to meet all performance and safety requirements before turning on the AC drives.
2. Turn the selector switch of the drive to the manual mode. This will allow you to operate the drive with the local controls.
3. Use the local display and programming panel to view and program the drive parameters. Refer to the programming manual to change the parameters listed below. List the parameter values that you select in the space provided.

Parameters/Functions

5, 6.   *Speed select* determines which one of six possible sources will control the drive output frequency with the speed selector switch.

0 = The local control panel potentiometer. 1 = A 0 to 10 V DC source. 2 = A 4 to 20 mA source. 3 = A pulse train source. 4 = A serial input. 5 = A remote speed potentiometer.

Set parameter 5 for 0 to +10 DC V source.

Set parameter 6 for either remote or local speed potentiometer.

16, 17, 18, 19, 20.   *Operating values* set the drive operating frequencies and voltages.

16 = _____ sets the minimum operating frequency between 0 and 120 hertz.

17 = _____ base frequency set to the nameplate values of motor.

18 = _____ base voltage set to the nameplate values of motor.

19 = _____ sets the maximum operating frequency between 0 and 250 hertz.

20 = _____ maximum voltage should be set equal to or greater than base voltage on parameter 18.

10, 12, 13.   *Stop select* parameter selects the stopping performance of the motor. 0—coast to stop, 1—DC brake to stop, and 2—ramp to stop.

10 = _____ sets coast to stop or DC brake to stop or ramp to stop.

12 = _____ sets a 0 to 15 seconds hold time upon stopping.

13 = _____ sets a 0 to 115 DC voltage applied to the motor to achieve braking.

7, 30. *Accel time* determines the time that it will take the drive to ramp (increase speed) from zero hertz to maximum frequency.

7 = _____ sets 1 to 600 seconds to ramp accel time #1 from zero to maximum frequency.

30 = _____ sets 1 to 600 seconds to ramp accel time #2, if used.

8, 31. *Decel time* determines the time that it will take to ramp (slow down) from maximum frequency to zero hertz.

8 = _____ sets 1 to 600 seconds to ramp decel time #1 from maximum to zero hertz.

31 = _____ sets 1 to 600 seconds to ramp decel time #2, if used.

32, 33, 34, 35. *Skip frequency bands* establish ranges of frequencies at which the drive will not operate. Each band establishes a range of frequencies at which the drive will not operate.

32 = _____ skip frequency band #1.

33 = _____ skip frequency band #2.

34 = _____ skip frequency band #3.

35 = _____ sets the plus or minus range of the frequency bands from 0 to 15 hertz.

43, 44. *Dwell frequency and time.* The drive will not follow the accel ramp to this frequency but jump directly to dwell setting. The drive then stays at this dwell frequency for a preset time, then ramps up or down. This will allow the motor to produce a higher starting torque.

43 = _____ sets the frequency the drive will jump to upon start from 0 to 120 hertz.

44 = _____ sets the time the drive will hold at dwell frequency from 0 to 10 seconds.

45. *Pulse Width Modulation (PWM).* This parameter will adjust the minimum carrier frequency used to generate the PWM output frequency. Increased PWM decreases audible motor noise and stability on a lightly loaded motor. Reduced PWM increases audible motor noise and stability on the motor.

45 = _____ sets the carrier frequency from 0.4 kHZ to 2 kHZ.

38. *Overload current* sets the overload protection of the motor at a set percentage of the current. The setting is 50 to 100 percent of rated output current. Timing begins when the output current rises above this parameter.

38 = _____ percentage of rated output current.

21, 22, 23, 24 *Reverse and Jog.* Select the source that determines the direction and jogging of the motor. These settings will control the operation of the drive from local or remote input devices.

21 = _____ local run.

22 = _____ reverse source.

23 = _____ jog source.

24 = _____ frequency used when jog is pressed.

When you have completed the programming on the drives, test the various parameters by operating the drive with the local control panel. Have your instructor present to verify the drive operaton.

PROGRAMMING

Detailed coverage of the various programming instructions is of great importance to the technologist who is confronted with designing and programming a control system. Therefore, the emphasis of this section is on detailed coverage of the logical instructions used in programming the programmable controller and its application to industrial control circuits. Examples of systems application of many instructions are presented to provide a basic idea of how these instructions could be used in real world practical situations.

OBJECTIVES

After completing this section, you should be able to:
- Design and program logic control circuits.
- Understand and apply relay, timing and counting instructions to form various control systems.
- Implement and apply comparison, compute, and file instructions to form complex control systems.
- Investigate the use of shift registers and sequencers to handle repetetive control systems.
- Use bit files to detect errors in automated processes.
- Apply the use of thumbwheel switches in various programming functions.
- Use a limit test instruction to generate forward and reverse sequences.
- Identify the basic forms of data and time movement in shift registers.
- Describe applications of digital-to-analog and analog-to-digital conversions.
- Define the basic characteristics of the PID instruction.
- Investigate the concept of structured text programming.

INTRODUCTION

Programming is very simply the process of telling the programmable controller exactly how to do a job. To do this, you must speak to the PLC in a language it can understand. Then it will faithfully perform each instruction it receives. It will do nothing that it is not instructed to do; therefore, you must tell the PLC absolutely everything that it must do, step-by-step.

In this manual, we will use the instructions necessary to be able to speak to the PLC in a vocabulary which it will understand. From these instructions, we will also be developing some programs that closely resemble the logic used in a hardwired control system relay ladder diagram.

Before we begin programming, we must look for a direction to follow for generating the necessary results we want to accomplish. This can be done by organizing our job into step-by-step sequence of operations. The sequence listed below illustrates these steps.

1. Defining the Circuit

In some cases, the circuit to be defined may be a complex industrial system which requires a staff of engineers and technicians to design and organize. In other cases, the job may be as simple as wiring a basic ON/OFF device. Either way, you generally start with only an idea about the desired results. Then, together with your knowledge of control circuits, software and hardware, you develop a clearer picture of what needs to be done and a definite direction to arrive at its solution.

Defining a circuit may seem obvious at times, but it is very important because it supplies the three fundamentals quantities needed to develop our programs:
1. The inputs we must supply.
2. The outputs we desire to control.
3. The logic that is required to control the circuit.

There are numerous control circuits are used in typical motor control applications. These common types of circuits will be used throughout this project manual.

2. Writing the Sequence

After you have defined your circuit and have connected your input and output devices to the I/O modules, you are ready to begin writing the program for your particular application. You can achieve the same results with a number of programs just as an electician can connect the same control circuit in a number of different ways to accomplish the same results. What is important is that you write your program so that you use your time efficiently so that the program operates in a safe and efficient manner. The first step this is to write a sequence in which your input and output devices can operate. Decide what the devices must do and what conditions must be true before these devices can begin operating. This will make programming less difficult because it will help you visualize the logic that is required to control the circuit. See Project 1.0, Program Logic.

3. Writing and Loading the Program

Once the circuit is well defined, it can be written down or coded. Coded means a series of instructions can be written and then implemented by the programmable controller. It is best to write down your program logic and identify the instruction addresses that you will be using. This will help you gain a sense of direction of where to start and help you to begin loading your program.

In loading your program, all your communications are made through a keyboard. It is important that you become familiar with what each key function accomplishes. Refer to your manufacturer's manual for information concerning the key functions of your PLC. When entering your instructions in the PLC you should be in the PROGRAM mode, all outputs are deenergized in this position and the machine controlled by the PLC will not operate.

4. Test and Run Program

Once you have completed entering your program, proceed to test your program. In the test mode, the program is tested under simulated operating conditions (instructions will highlight on the screen). Inputs are active and recognized by the processor, but user output devices are not energized. All outputs are disabled in this position. The laboratory simulator can be used to implement and demonstrate all the projects. If everything checks out correctly, you can return to the program mode and document your instructions. This is to avoid any confusion later if you want to make any changes or expand your program. At this point, you should also save your program on your own disk.

You are now ready to run your program. At this stage, you should check with your instructor to assure that all necessary steps have been taken to meet all performance and safety requirements.

Safety

1. Motor starters should be connected and tested before any loads or motors are connected.
2. All limits should be checked and tested for proper operation. Overloads, stops and limits should be verified.
3. Do not work with any live power. Always disconnect the circuit before doing any connections.
4. Follow the manufacturer's performance and safety requirements.
5. Have your instructor check your work and be present at all times when connecting or operating your program.

STOP–START (PLC)

Purpose: To develop a program on the PLC for a stop–start pushbutton control circuit controlling a three-phase motor starter.

After completion of this project, you should be able to:
- Use XIC (examine input close) instructions to program stop and start pushbuttons.
- Program a real world starter and the seal–in contact.
- Use a latch/unlatch instruction.
- Use an MCR instruction.
- Program the logic functions AND, OR, NOT, and MEMORY.

To preview an example and a brief description of each instruction that will be used in this project, refer to Appendix A: Relay Type and Program Control Instructions. XIC, XIO, OTE, OTL, OTU, MCR.

Programmable controllers have many of the capabilities of hardwired relay control systems. Control functions similar to those available with relays are provided by the examine and the output instructions.

 There are two examine instructions: ON (–] [–) and OFF (–] / [–). When the *examine off* or *examine on* instruction is given a bit address in memory, the instruction can indirectly examine the status of its corresponding input device. The status of the bit will be a one or zero reflecting the ON (true) or OFF (false) condition, respectively, of the input/output device. See figure 6.1, Examine On, Examine Off and Output Instructions. The output instruction tells the processor to turn an addressed memory bit on when the rung conditions are true. This memory bit will determine the on or off status of an output device when addressed to the output terminal.

Stop–Start Pushbutton

In programming, the same instruction is used for the stop and start pushbutton devices because XIC instructions do not differentiate between normally open and normally closed devices. Instead, they look at the ON or OFF condition of the device and set a bit in memory depending on that condition.

 In figure 6.2, notice that the stop button is programmed with a normally open XIC instruction (–] [–). Also, the start button is programmed with a normally open XIC instruction (–] [–). The normally closed stop button (I:000/11) is true (ON) when it is not depressed. The normally open start button (I:000/10) is tRUE (ON) when it is depressed. This creates the same condition on both the stop and start button.

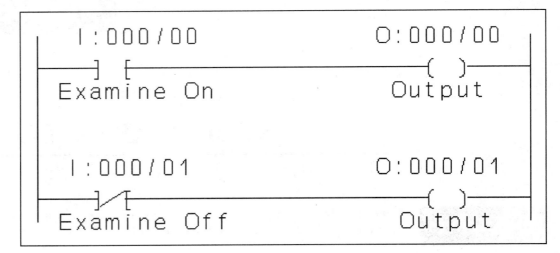

Figure 6.1. Examine ON/OFF and Output Instructions.

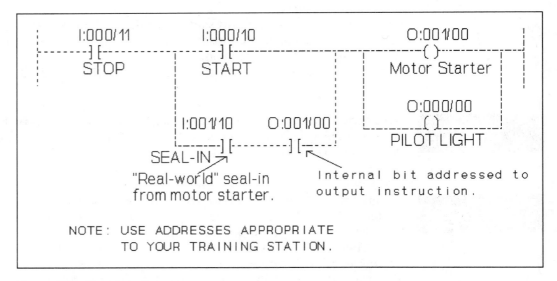

Figure 6.2. Stop-Start Program.

Seal in Safety

There are various methods of programming seal–in control circuits with a motor control starter. *Safety* is the determining factor in the programming method.

One method is to program the real world seal–in contacts of the starter in series (anded) with an internal bit addressed to the output. Because of program and I/O scan times, it is important to have both the hardwired real world seal–in and the internal seal–in within the circuit. Notice in figure 6.2, that Address I:001/ 10 represents a real–world hardwired seal–in contact of the motor starter.

The purpose of the hardwired seal–in contact is to physically break the control circuit for any condition that might turn off the starter, such as an overload. An internal seal–in by itself would not sense the starter opening. As a result, internal seal–ins would remain closed. Manually resetting the overloads would start the motor immediately and possibly cause an unsafe condition.

Another method is to connect the overload contacts of the starter as an input device. Then the overload contacts can be programmed in the control circuit. Many industries require both the overload contacts and the real world seal–in contacts to be connected as an input and programmed in the circuit.

Throughout the projects and experiments in this manual, we will use one method or the other and sometimes both. The project and the experiments used in this project will demonstrate the logic concepts and techniques that can be applied with the other projects in this manual.

PROGRAM LOGIC

1. An input instruction for the normally closed momentary stop pushbutton. When pressed, the circuit will be false and the motor will stop.
2. An input instruction for the normally opened momentary start pushbutton. When pressed, the circuit will be true and the motor will start.
3. A real world seal–in from the motor starter, identified as an input and connected to an input module.
4. A full voltage motor starter with a 24 V DC coil and its overload contacts connected as an input device.
5. An output instruction for a 24 V pilot light which is to be ON when the motor is on (ON–when–on).
6. Pressing the start button seals in the motor until the stop button is depressed.

PROCEDURES

Note: Read Experiment 6.6 before starting this project.

1. Create a program directory called PROJECT6 and change the file name to Stop-Start. Proceed to monitor file (f8) and construct your program.
2. Develop a program on the PLC for the stop–start circuit as shown in figure 6.2.

Note: Check the addresses of the starters in your work station. The addresses of the starters at your station might be different than the addresses on the diagram.

3. Observe the first instruction –] [– I:000/11. This is an XIC open instruction addressed to a normally closed stop pushbutton input. The processor will scan this input and see it as closed. Therefore, it will set the XIC instruction bit to a one and allow power flow through to the next instruction.
4. Notice the next instruction –] [– I:000/10. This is an XIC instruction addressed to a normally open start pushbutton. The processor will scan the start button input and see it as open. Only when the start button is pressed (closed) will it set the XIC bit to a one and make the rung true. This is a technique that is often difficult to analyze. The same type of instruction is used for a stop and start pushbutton. You can verify this operation when you run the circuit.
5. Another technique used in this project is the real world seal–in contacts (–] [– I:001/10). These are programmed in series with an internal bit addressed to the output. See safety seal–in discussion.
6. Once you have completed the previous procedures, accept your rung and proceed to test your program. In the test mode you will see your program operate on the monitor only. The starter and the seal–in contacts will not turn on.

   If everything seems correct in the test mode, change to the run mode and operate your program with the motor starters only. Check the overloads and the stop circuit. If it works properly, proceed to run the motor. Have your instructor present at this stage and follow all safety procedures.

7. The next step is to document your instructions and your rung. You can use the documentation shown in figure 6.2 as an example. Enter the rung comment as Project 6, stop–start. Once your documentation is complete, save your documentation and your program to a floppy disk.

8. Now that you have successfully completed the first part of Project 6, to test your understanding of the concepts covered in this project, proceed to complete the experiments listed below. Each experiment should be separately identified with rung documentation. When you have completed all of the experiments, save your program to your floppy disk again.

9. The final step is to create a report, title the report with your name, and print your report. Have your instructor check the completed report.

SEQUENCE START

Name _____ Date _____

Approved by _____

Design and add to the above Project 6 program, the following circuit. See Experiment 1.3 for the ladder diagram of this experiment.

1. A second motor starter (#2) with its own stop–start. This second motor starter will not be able to start unless the first motor starter is running .
2. A pilot light to indicate when the motor (#1) is OFF. Light is ON when motor (#1) is OFF.
3. Use appropriate addresses for pushbuttons and the motor starter.

**EXPERIMENT
6.2**

LATCH/UNLATCH

Name _____   Date _____

Approved by _____

Enter the latch/unlatch program shown in figure 6.3. The purpose of this experiment is to familiarize you with a latch/unlatch instruction.

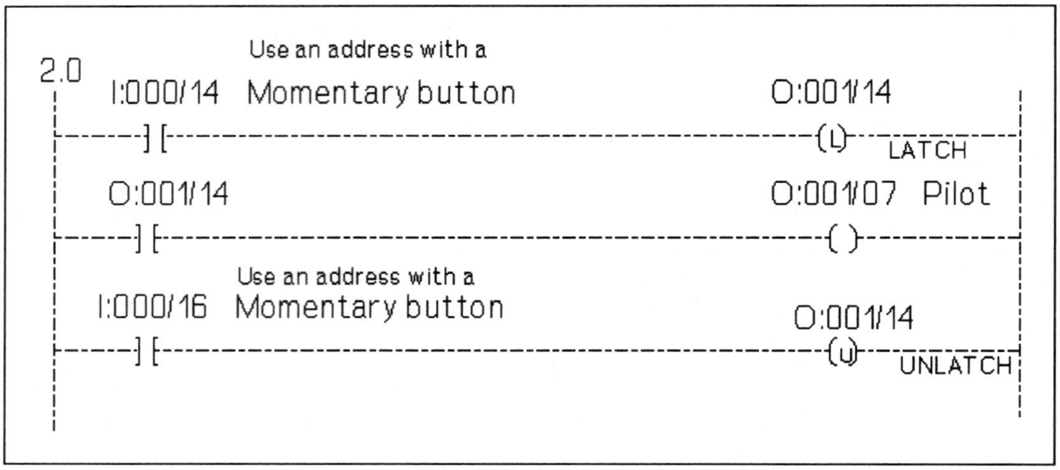

Figure 6.3. Latch/Unlatch Program.

1. Output latch and unlatch instructions are retentive output instructions. They are usually used in a pair for any data table bit they control.
2. When you have entered the program, try to operate the program. Remember to use addresses that are appropriate to your simulator.
3. First, press the latch rung pushbutton and observe the latch output. It should remain ON even after you release the pushbutton to make the rung false.
4. Next, press the unlatch pushbutton. This should unlatch the output and remain unlatched until the latch is pressed again.
5. The seal–in feature is important because you can seal in a bit with a momentary pulse. With this capability, you seal and unseal bits at various times using counters or timers. Such instructions are covered in later experiments.

| EXPERIMENT 6.3 | **MASTER CONTROL RESET (MCR)** |

Name _____   Date _____

Approved by _____

Enter the MCR program shown in figure 6.4. The purpose of this experiment is to familiarize you with an MCR instruction.

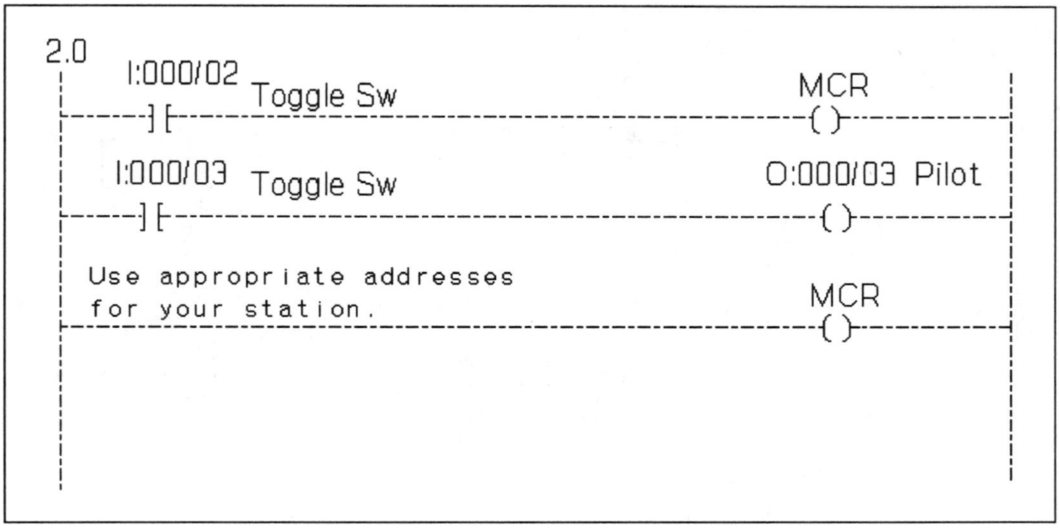

```
2.0   I:000/02                                    MCR
      ---] [----- Toggle Sw ----------------------( )--------

      I:000/03                               O:000/03 Pilot
      ---] [----- Toggle Sw ----------------------( )--------

      Use appropriate addresses                   MCR
      for your station.                           ( )--------
```

Figure 6.4. Master Control Reset Program.

1. The master control reset instruction (MCR) is an output instruction. It lets the processor enable or inhibit a zone of ladder program according to the program logic.
2. When you have entered the program, try operating it.
3. First, turn on the toggle switch controlling the MCR instruction. Proceed to verify the operation of your ON/OFF circuit located in the MCR zone. The circuits in the MCR zone should be enabled.
4. Next, turn off the switch controlling MCR instruction and try operating the circuit in the MCR zone. The circuits should be inhibited. Only the circuit outside the MCR zone would function properly.
5. You can use MCR instructions to create program zones that turn off all non–retentive outputs in the zone.

   Note: It is important to know that this should not be used as a substitute for a hardwired master control relay that provides emergency stop capabilities. Read the safety precautions in the instruction set manual.

HAND–AUTO

Name _____ Date _____

Approved by _____

Convert the electrical circuit diagram shown in figure 6.5 to a PLC program. Program the circuit with the following parameters:

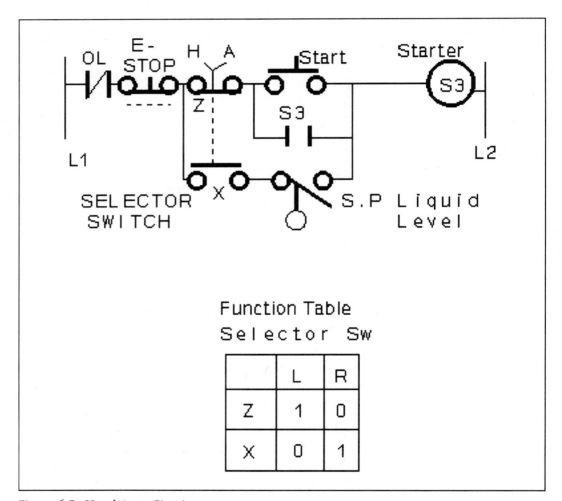

Figure 6.5. Hand-Auto Circuit.

1. Use a toggle switch as a selector switch. A toggle switch addressed to an XIC (-) [-] and XIO (-] / [-) instruction can be used as a two selector position switch. Select the stop-start pushbutton for manual control or select a liquid level switch for automatic control of a starter (S3). Use a toggle switch to simulate a liquid level switch.
2. Follow the same procedure as in the stop-start circuit of Project 6 for the seal-in contacts.
3. The stop circuit should be a push/pull E-stop circuit. If this is not available on your trainer, use a ON/OFF toggle switch for the stop circuit.

EXPERIMENT 6.5

NON-SEQUENTIAL LIGHTS

Name _____   Date _____

Approved by _____

Convert and program the circuit of the electrical Experiment 1.5. This experiment uses three momentary start buttons to control its own light. Follow the steps listed below:

1. Pressing any start pushbutton would energize and seal its corresponding light. Only one light can be sealed on at any one time. Use an output instruction (OTE) to activate the lights on your trainer.

2. When more than one button is pressed simultaneously, corresponding lights will be turned on. However, only one light will remain on when the buttons are released.

EXPERIMENT 6.6	**LOGIC CIRCUIT LAB**

Name _____ Date _____

Approved by _____

This experiment can be used as an optional beginning project to acquire skills in programming and familiarization of the software. It could also be used as an extra assignment for the student who needs additional practice in programming ladder diagram circuits. The experiment is a combinational circuit incorporating various ladder logic concepts. Only the basic examine ON/OFF and output instructions are used. See figure 6.6. Check with your instructor on the requirements of this lab.

Follow the steps listed below:

1. Create a separate program directory named EXP6_6 and identify the file name as "Logic."
2. Program the first rung of Experiment 6.6 (AND logic) shown below. Use addresses pertaining to your training station.
3. Once you have completed the previous procedures, change to the run mode and operate your program. Check the various AND logic concepts of your program.
4. If everything works properly and you understand the concepts involved in this rung, enter the next rung of the program.
5. In program mode, enter the OR logic rung, then change to the run mode and check your program.
6. Continue this procedure until the program is complete.
7. Save your program to your disk and check with your instructor on the documentation and printing of this program.

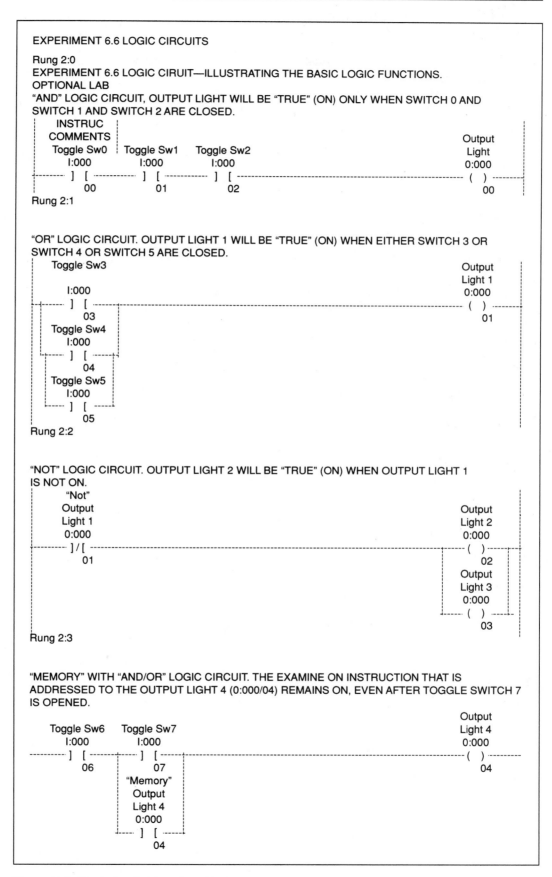

EXPERIMENT 6.6 LOGIC CIRCUITS

Rung 2:0
EXPERIMENT 6.6 LOGIC CIRUIT—ILLUSTRATING THE BASIC LOGIC FUNCTIONS.
OPTIONAL LAB
"AND" LOGIC CIRCUIT, OUTPUT LIGHT WILL BE "TRUE" (ON) ONLY WHEN SWITCH 0 AND
SWITCH 1 AND SWITCH 2 ARE CLOSED.

```
        INSTRUC
        COMMENTS                                                 Output
     Toggle Sw0    Toggle Sw1    Toggle Sw2                      Light
       I:000         I:000         I:000                         0:000
   ---- ] [ -------- ] [ -------- ] [ --------------------------- ( ) ------
         00            01            02                            00
```
Rung 2:1

"OR" LOGIC CIRCUIT. OUTPUT LIGHT 1 WILL BE "TRUE" (ON) WHEN EITHER SWITCH 3 OR
SWITCH 4 OR SWITCH 5 ARE CLOSED.

```
     Toggle Sw3                                                 Output
                                                                Light 1
       I:000                                                    0:000
   ----- ] [ ----------------------------------------------------( ) -------
          03                                                       01
     Toggle Sw4
       I:000
   ----- ] [ -----
          04
     Toggle Sw5
       I:000
   ----- ] [ -----
          05
```
Rung 2:2

"NOT" LOGIC CIRCUIT. OUTPUT LIGHT 2 WILL BE "TRUE" (ON) WHEN OUTPUT LIGHT 1
IS NOT ON.

```
      "Not"
      Output                                                   Output
      Light 1                                                  Light 2
      0:000                                                    0:000
   ----- ]/[ ----------------------------------------------------( ) ------
          01                                                      02
                                                               Output
                                                               Light 3
                                                               0:000
                                                             ------( ) ------
                                                                    03
```
Rung 2:3

"MEMORY" WITH "AND/OR" LOGIC CIRCUIT. THE EXAMINE ON INSTRUCTION THAT IS
ADDRESSED TO THE OUTPUT LIGHT 4 (0:000/04) REMAINS ON, EVEN AFTER TOGGLE SWITCH 7
IS OPENED.

```
                                                               Output
     Toggle Sw6    Toggle Sw7                                  Light 4
       I:000         I:000                                     0:000
   ---- ] [ -------- ] [ ------------------------------------------( ) ------
          06            07                                          04
                    "Memory"
                    Output
                    Light 4
                    0:000
                  ---- ] [ -----
                       04
```

Figure 6.6. Basic Logic Functions Program.

RUN AND JOG

OBJECTIVES

Purpose: To develop a program using bit instruction for pushbutton control of a motor starter to either run continuously or jog.
- Utilize internal bit/word instruction (B3/0).
- Use bit instruction to replace relay operations.
- Program run/jog circuits.
- Investigate bit modify and move instructions

REFERENCE READING

To preview an example and a brief description of each instruction used in this project, refer to Appendix A: Relay Type and Bit Modify/Move Instructions. XIC, XIO, OTE, BTD, MOV, MVM.

DISCUSSION

Jogging or *inching* are terms which describe the frequent starting and stopping of a motor for short periods of time. Jogging is used to position materials small distances each time the motor starts. Jogging is accomplished by removing or bypassing the seal-in contacts in the control circuit.

In the previous project, we used momentary pushbutton to control the motor starter for running. In this project, we will use a momentary pushbutton to control the motor starter for jogging and a momentary pushbutton to control a relay for sealing and running the motor. This type of circuit is called a *relay jog*. See figure 7.1.

In PLC programming, there are many times when instructions are internal to the computer. These instructions perform internal logic functions but do not control an output directly. An instruction that does this is called a *bit/word instruction*. Bit instruction can be addressed as a single bit address (B3/0) or as a 16-bit word address (B3:0).

In figure 7.1, the bit instruction (B3/0) does not directly control an output device. Instead, it is used logically in the program to control other instructions. In this case, it is used to seal in the circuit, much as an electromechanical relay and its associated contacts would be used to seal in the control circuit.

PROGRAM LOGIC

1. An input instruction for the normally closed momentary master stop button. When stop is pressed, the circuit will be false and motor will stop.
2. An input instruction for the normally open momentary run button.
3. An input instruction for the normally open jog pushbutton.
4. An output instruction for the motor starter coil. Overloads wired in series with the coil.
5. An output instruction for the pilot light which is to be ON only when the motor is in the RUN mode.

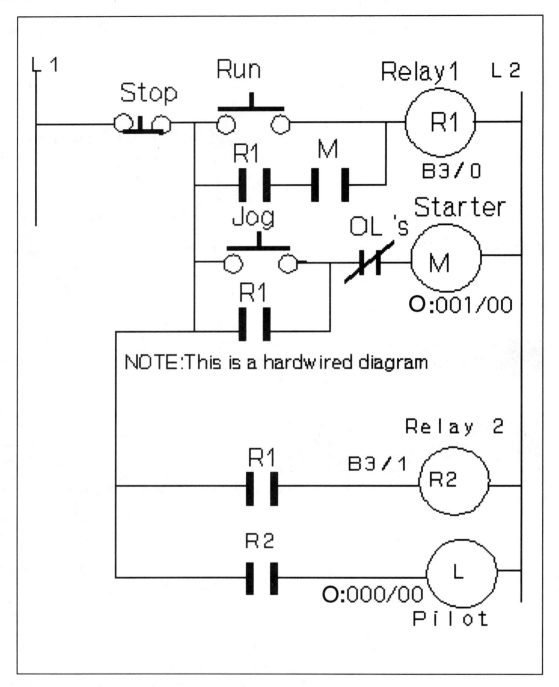

Figure 7.1. Run-Jog Circuit.

6. A bit word storage output is used to seal in the motor.
7. A real world seal in from the motor starter, identified as an input and connected in series with the internal seal-in.
8. Pressing the run button seals in the motor until the stop is depressed.
9. Pressing the jog button allows motor to run only when pushbutton is held in. Releasing the jog button stops the motor.

PROCEDURES

1. Create a new program directory (PROJECT7) and identify the file as run-jog. Proceed to monitor the file for program edits.
2. Develop a program on your PLC for the run/jog circuit as shown in figure 7.1. Use instruction addresses that are pertinent to your system. Refer to your manufacturer's data book for programming instructions.
3. Observe the output instruction -(   )- (B3/0) on your first rung. This bit file address is used to replace the relay coil in the hardwired diagram. Its purpose is to provide auxiliary seal in -]   [- instructions similar to the seal-in relay contacts. The bit file can be used for internal logic programming. When addressed as a single bit, the forward slash is used (B3/0). Also, it can be programmed as a full sixteen bit word by using the colon (B3:0).
4. Notice the real world seal-in -]   [- I:000/02 is still programmed into the circuit to prevent an accidental start by resetting overloads (see discussion in Project 1). The other output -(   )- O:000/00 in the next rung is addressed to a real world starter.
5. Another concept is the auxiliary contact (R) controlling a second relay (R2). In a hardwired connection, this could be a different voltage relay and light. With the PLC, just use another internal bit (B3/1) for relay 2.
6. Once you have completed the above procedures, accept your rung and proceed to test your program. In the test mode you will see your program operate on the monitor only. If everything seems correct in the test mode, change to the run mode and operate your program with the motor starters only. If it works properly, connect and run the motor. Check with your instructor at this point.
7. The next step is to document your instructions and your rung. Enter the rung comment as Project 7 Run/Jog. Once your documentation is complete, save your documentation and program to your floppy disk.
8. The final step is to create a report. Title the report with your name and print your report. Have your instructor check the completed report.

REVIEW

Now that you have successfully completed the first part of Project 7, to test your understanding of the concepts covered in this project, proceed to complete the experiments listed below. Each experiment should be separately identified with rung documentation. When you have completed all of the experiments, save your program to your floppy disk again.

EXPERIMENT

7.1

SELECTOR JOG

Name _____   Date _____

Approved by _____

With separate rungs, continue to program the circuit shown in figure 7.2. on Project 7. Use a two-position selector switch and a momentary start pushbutton to control motor 2 in the following sequence:

1. Turn selector left = pressing the start pushbutton, motor 2 would start and continue to run. Contactor and pilot light run continuously unless E-stop is in a depressed position.
2. Turn selector right = pressing the start button would jog the motor starter M2. Contactor and pilot light are OFF in this position.

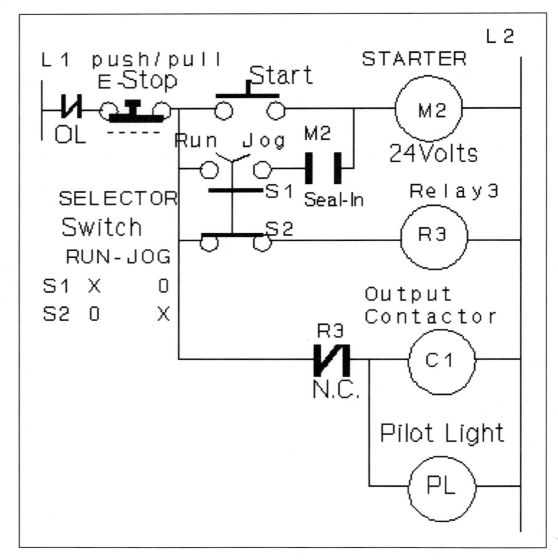

Figure 7.2. Selector Jog Circuit.

<table>
<tr><td>**EXPERIMENT**
7.2</td><td>**BIT MOVING**

Name _____ Date _____

Approved by _____</td></tr>
</table>

The purpose of this experiment is to familiarize yourself with the process of moving bits of information in a program. Program the circuit in figure 7.3. Use a bit field distribute (BTD), a move (MOV) and a masked move (MVM) instructions to perform the following function:

Note: Check your input/output addresses. They could be different than the figure diagram. Use the appropriate addresses of your trainer.

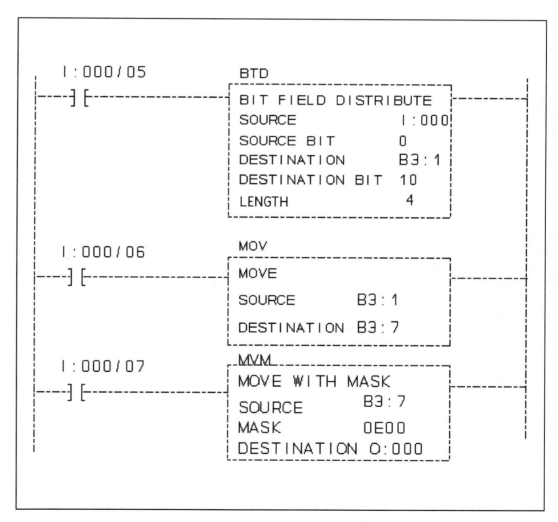

Figure 7.3. Bit-Move Instructions.

When you have completed entering the program, change to the run mode and observe the bit movement on the screen in the data monitor binary mode. Check your program as follows:

1. Change the source bits with switches 00 to 03. Move that information with switch 05. Turning on switch 05 will move the lower four bits of I:0 to B3:1, starting at bit 10.
2. Close switch 06 to move the bits at B3:1 to B3:7.
3. Turning on switch 07 will move the bits from B3:7 to the output lights O:000. The lights will operate only if the masked value allows it. In this case, the masked value will allow three of the bits to filter through.
4. Continue this process until you feel comfortable in understanding the movement of bits in the program.

BAG CONVEYOR

OBJECTIVES

Purpose: To develop a program for controlling the ON/OFF time of a bagging conveyor, utilizing TON (timer-on) delay timers.

After completion of this project, you should be able to:
- Understand the concept of timers.
- Investigate the jump (JMP) to label (LBL) instructions.
- Develop an understanding of how to use timers to control a process.

REFERENCE READING

To preview an example and a brief description of each instruction that will be used in this project, refer to Appendix A: Timer and Program Control Instructions. TON, TOF, RTO, JMP, LBL.

DISCUSSION

Timer instructions are output instructions internal to the processor. They provide many of the capabilities available with timing relays and solid state timing/counting devices. Usually conditioned by input instructions, timers keep track of timed intervals. See figure 8.1. Preset value (PR) specifies the number of timed intervals

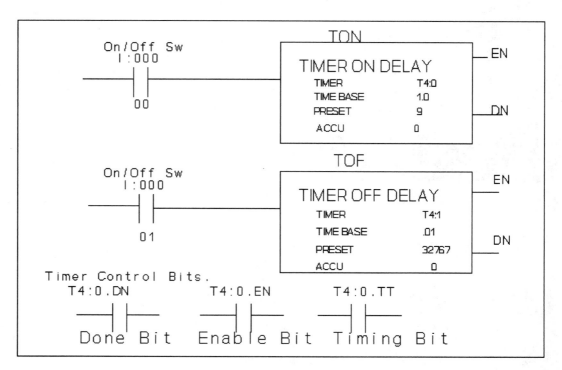

Figure 8.1. Timer Instructions.

that must be reach before the processor sets a complete bit (DN) and your ladder program can take action. Accumulated value (AC) is the number of time intervals that have elapsed.

The timer on-delay (TON) instruction can be used to turn a device ON or OFF once an interval is timed out. As long as the rung condition remains true the timer increments its accumulated value for each interval. When the accumulated value equals the preset value the timer stops and sets the control bits.

The timer off-delay (TOF) instruction varies from the TON in that it begins to time an interval as soon as the rung goes false. As long as its rung condition remain false, the TOF instruction continues to time until the accumulated value equals the preset value. When the TOF instruction times out it sets the control bits

Project

The project involves the use of timers and photo-electric eyes to control a conveyor fill system. See figure 8.2 bagging conveyor. Empty bags move along a conveyor, when the bags are at the appropriate location the conveyor stops and a fill process begins. When the fill process is completed, the conveyor restarts and the bags continue along the conveyor for further processing.

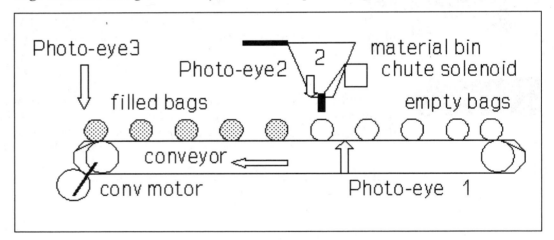

Figure 8.2. Bagging Conveyor System.

PROGRAM LOGIC

Follow the elements of the conveyor flow chart in figure 8.3 to guide you in organizing the rungs in the program.

1. Element 1.0 identifies the starting methods that are used to start the conveyor.
   A. Use an MCR instruction operated by a toggle switch as your first rung. Next, use a stop-start circuit with the same toggle switch for the stop and a manually operated start pushbutton to activate the output for the conveyor. Use a magnetic starter to operate the conveyor.
   B. The automatic start can be a normally open timer timing bit (T4:3.TT) in parallel with the seal-in contact of the starter.
2. In Element 2.0, a photo-eye is the next device that will be activated when the first bag reaches the fill area.Use a toggle switch to simulate the photo-eye. This will activate a timer on delay (T4:1) with a preset of one second. The reason is to allow the bag to center itself over the fill chute. Use a TT bit to seal the timer.

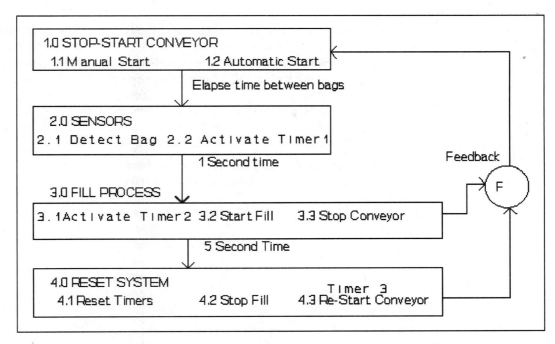

Figure 8.3. Conveyor Flow Chart.

3. In the next step, Element 3.0 has three functions:
   A. To activate a second timer on delay T4:2.
   B. To stop the conveyor.
   C. To begin fill for a period of five seconds. Assure that a bag is in the correct place.
4. Element 4.0 is the reset period. Once timer (T4:2) stops the following occurs:
   A. The fill process should stop.
   B. The timers should reset.
   C. The conveyor should re-start and run until the next bag reaches the photo-eye. A timer (T4:3) is used to restart the conveyor. Electromechanical starters are slower to activate in comparison to plc instructions, therefore they need a minimun amount of time to activate the coil.
5. **Note:** Photo-eye three could be used to activate a counter for counting the number of filled bags. This option could be added into the project after completion of project 10 Up/Dn counters. This project can be accomplish using the simulator, output lights can be used for the solenoid and a motor starter for the conveyor. Pushbuttons can be used for stop/start circuit and toggle switches for the photoelectric controls.

PROCEDURES

1. Develop a program on the PLC for the automated bagging system as described in the flow chart of figure 8.3. and shown in the conveyor system of figure 8.2. The timing rungs are described below. You must complete the remaining program to make the circuit functional.
2. The first step in the program is the manual and the automatic starting circuit. You first rung should be an MCR instruction operated by the stop switch. For the next rung, use a stop-start pushbutton circuit for starting and stopping the conveyor. This circuit is similar to the circuit shown in figure 6.2.

Your stop switch is addressed the same as the MCR rung input switch. Use one of your motor starters and its seal-in contact to run the conveyor.

3. The next step is the fill process. As the empty bags advance on the conveyor to the point where photo-eye 1 detects a bag, the following should occur:

Photo-eye 1 activates a timer-on delay T4:1. Use a T4:1.TT bit of this timer in parallel with the photo-eye 1 to seal in your time. See figure 8.4. This timer allows for a one second delay to set-up the bags for the filling process.

Note: You can use photoeye one to activate a shutdown timer if bags remain stuck in front of the photoeye.

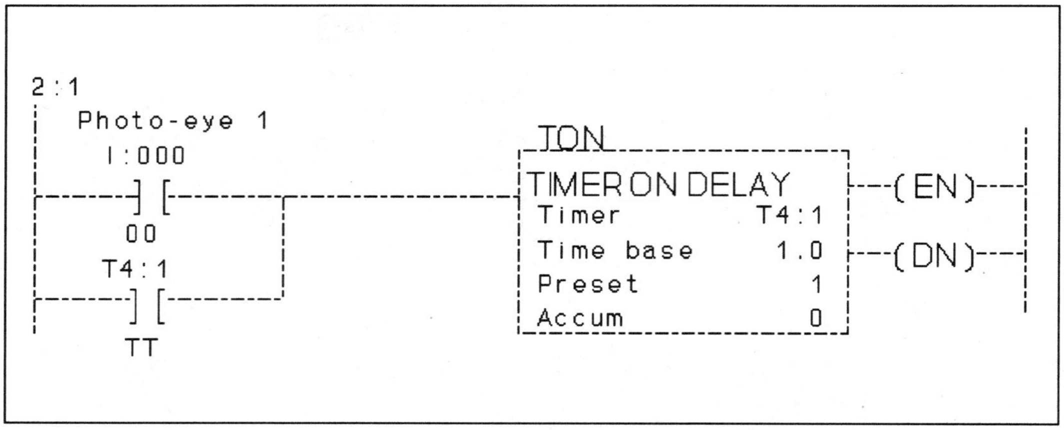

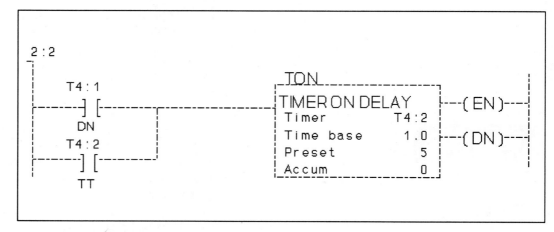

Figure 8.4. Set-Up Timer Rung.

4. A second timer-on delay (T4:2) is activated by the timer T4:1.Done bit. Seal this timer with its TT bit. Preset time is five seconds. See figure 8.5. This timer is to control the solenoid for a preset fill time.

Note: Insert a normally closed T4:2.TT bit from this timer in the start conveyor circuit to stop the conveyor while the fill is in process.

Figure 8.5. Fill Timer Rung.

In a separate rung, use a T4:2.EN bit to activate a fill solenoid for a five second fill time. In this rung, photo-eye 2 should be inserted as a limit to prevent the fill if bag is not positioned correctly and a T4:2.DN bit to prevent fill longer than the preset time.

5. When the fill process is completed, a third timer T4:3 is used to start the conveyor automatically when the bag is filled. Preset this timer for 20 and set the time base for 0.01 seconds. Seal this timer with its T4:3.TT bit. See figure 8.6.

Note: Use a T4:3.TT bit from this timer in parallel with the start pushbutton circuit to restart the conveyor and repeat the process.

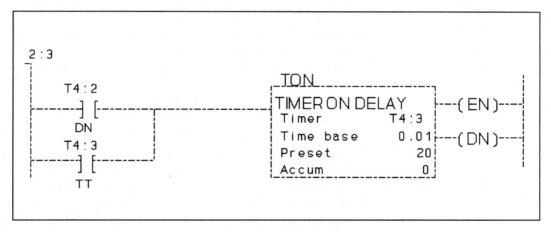

Figure 8.6. Reset Timer Rung.

6. Once you have completed the previous procedures, proceed to run your program. Start the program with your start pushbutton. Try closing and opening your photoeye 1 switch. Check the timers to see if your process is working correctly. Follow the steps in the program logic to check your circuit.If everything works correctly, have your instructor check your program. Document all your instructions and save your program to your disk.

REVIEW

Now that you have successfully completed the first part of Project 8, to test your understanding of the concepts covered in this project, proceed to complete the experiments listed below. When you have completed all of the experiments save your program and your documentation to your floppy disk again. The final step is to create and print your report. Have your instructor check the completed report.

EXPERIMENT 8.1	**TIMED MOTOR SEQUENCE**

Name _____ Date _____

Approved by _____

A manufacturing plant wants you to program a circuit that would start three motors in a timed sequence. Modify and program the circuit in electrical Experiment 4.2 to meet the requirements of this experiment. Pressing the start button will energize timer #4, #5 and #6 in the following sequence:

1. Timer-off delay #4 activates starter #1 to start the motor #1 immediately.
2. When timer-on delay #5 times out, starter #2 will be energized to start motor #2 and timer number #6.
3. When timer-on delay #6 times out, starter #3 will be energized to start motor #3, this completes the sequence.
4. All three motors are now running. Pressing the stop buttton will initiate the following:
   A. Motor #2 and #3 immediately stop.
   B. Motor #1 continues to run for an additional seven seconds.

After the time elapses motor #1 stops and all motors are off.

Notes: On all the experiments, continue from the last timer used in the project and address the timers in ascending order. Place a jump (LBL) to label (LBL) instructions as shown below around Experiment 8.1. This will allow you to create a zone around the experiment and re-use the pushbuttons again. When the rung condition for the JMP output is true, the processor jumps forward to the corresponding label instruction and resumes program execution at the label.

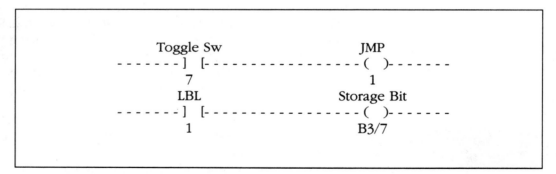

Figure 8.7. Jump to Label Instructions.

EXPERIMENT 8.2

TIMED PRESS CIRCUIT

Name _____   Date _____

Approved by _____

In your plant there is a cutter press that requires a safety circuit where an operator is required to use both hands to operate the press. Modify and program the circuit shown in figure 4.4 to meet the requirements of this experiment.

1. Two pushbuttons must be pressed simultaneously to activate the press solenoid.
2. Two on-delay timers are required to control the amount of time of each pushbutton when pressed.
3. A timer off-delay to control the period of ON time of the press solenoid.
4. Place a JMP to LBL instruction around this experiment similar to above Experiment 8.1.

CYCLE TIMER

Name _____   Date _____

Approved by _____

Program the circuit shown in figure 8.8. The circuit uses a timer-on/timer-off delay to operate as an oscillator (repeat continuously). Run the program and observe the timer accumulated values. They should alternate their accumulated values 0 to 100. The light will also cycle ON for a second then OFF for a second.

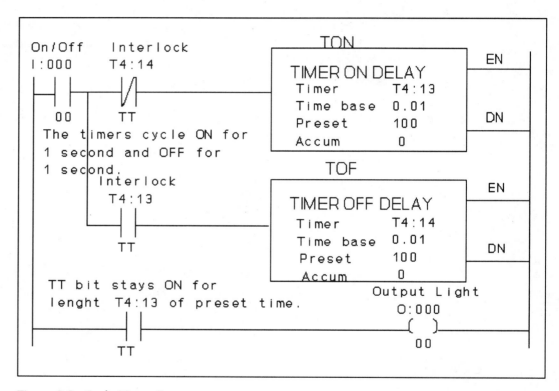

Figure 8.8. Cycle Timer Program.

When you have completed and tested this circuit, proceed to advance editing, select and copy this oscillator circuit to a paste file. Name your paste file OSC. Your instructor can assist you in this procedure.

NON-SEQUENTIAL STARTS

Name _____   Date _____

Approved by _____

Design and program a circuit that will operate three motor starters. Each starter will have its own stop/start pushbutton. Because of high starting currents and machinery requirements, the circuit needs to operate as follows:

1. Pressing any of the starts will start the appropriate starter connected to this start button.
2. Once a starter has been turned ON, no other starter can be started for a set timed period, depending on the preset of a timer.
3. When the preset value of this timer has elapsed, any of the other two motors can be started.
4. Once a second motor is started, the last motor starter cannot be started for a set timed period.
5. After the timed period has elapsed, the third motor can be started. All three starters would be ON.
6. A timed period should occur between any of the starts, regardless of the order that the starters are started.

FORWARD REVERSE (OFF-DELAY)

OBJECTIVES

Purpose: Program timer-off delay instructions to prevent a forward/reverse motor starter from restarting in the opposite direction for a preset period of time. After performing this experiment, you should be able to:

- Program timer-off delay instructions with a forward/reverse starter.
- Investigate the jump to label instructions.

REFERENCE READING

To preview an example and a brief description of each instruction that will be used in this project, refer to Appendix A. Timer and Program Control Instructions. TON, TOF, JMP, LBL.

DISCUSSION

In many instances, because of the nature of the equipment, it is not advisable to reverse a motor too quickly from one direction to another. This project uses two timer-off delay controls in the amount of time the motor remains OFF after a stop. The circuit inhibits a restart in the opposite direction for a preset period of time.

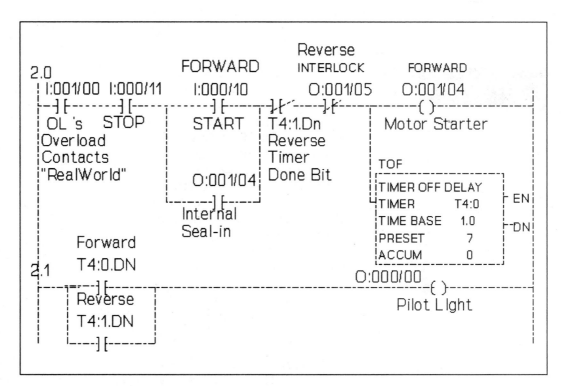

Figure 9.1. Forward Direction Program.

Figure 9.1 illustrates a timer-off delay used to prevent the motor from restarting in the opposite direction (reverse) too quickly. Stopping the motor makes the forward rung false (OFF). The timer-off delay instructions start a time interval as soon as its rung condition goes false. As long as its rung condition remains false, the TOF continues to time until the accumulated value equals the preset value. During that timed period, the reverse rung (not shown) TOF done bit would remain open until the timed period expired, preventing a start in the opposite direction for a specified time.

Project

The purpose of this project is to program a forward and reverse starter using a timer-off delay instruction to interlock the opposite direction from starting after a stop has occured. A period of time must elapse after stopping from either direction, before restarting in the opposite direction. Project 4, figure 4.3, is the electro-mechanical equivalent of this program.

Another type of instruction that will be used in this project is a jump to label instruction. Jumping forward to a label saves scan time by omitting a section of the program until needed. This allows you to use the same switches in two different locations.

PROGRAM LOGIC

1. An input instruction for the normally closed momentary stop button for stopping in either direction.
2. An input instruction for the normally open momentary start button for starting the forward and the reverse.
3. Internal instructions for the normally closed electrical interlocks to prevent trying to run in both direction at the same time.
4. Real world overload for both the forward and reverse.
5. A pilot light to indicate that motor can be restarted when light goes OFF.

PROCEDURES

1. Create a program directory named (PROJECT9) and name your file forward reverse. Develop a program on the PLC for the forward/reverse circuit. Use appropriate addresses pertaining to starters at your work station.
2. For the first step, enter the program shown in figure 9.1. The first rung is the controls for the forward direction only. Keep in mind that the addresses at your work station might be different. The second rung is the controls to activate a pilot light in either the forward or reverse. This pilot will remain ON until the starter is deactivated.
3. Next, enter a duplicate of the first rung (2.0) for the reverse output. The only difference will be the appropriate addresses for all the instructions in this reverse rung.
4. Notice the inhibit bits -[/]- t4:0.dn, and t4:1.dn. These bits will inhibit the circuit and prevent it from running in the opposite direction for a preset period of time after stop has occured.
5. Another technique used in this project is the interlocks -[/]- O:001/04 and O:001/05. Interlocks are inserted in the forward and reverse rungs as a safety precaution to prevent the motor from trying to run in both directions at the same time.
6. The next step is to place the jump to label zone shown in figure 9.2 around this project. This will allow you to selectively jump over this section of the

program. When the rung containing the jump (JMP) instruction is true the processor jumps over successive rungs until it reaches the rung that contains the label (LBL) instruction with the same number. The processor resumes executing at the label rung.

7. Once you have completed the previous procedures (don't forget to save), proceed to test your program with the starters only. If everything works correctly, check with your instructor for testing and running the motor. Running a motor is not necessary for this project. When you run your program, pressing the stop button should prevent you from restarting in the opposite direction for seven seconds.

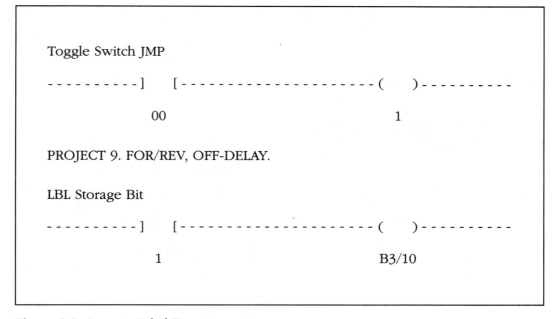

Toggle Switch JMP

\- - - - - - - - -]   [- (   ) - - - - - - - - - -

00   1

PROJECT 9. FOR/REV, OFF-DELAY.

LBL Storage Bit

\- - - - - - - - -]   [- (   ) - - - - - - - - - -

1   B3/10

Figure 9.2. Jump to Label Zone Instructions.

REVIEW

Now that you have successfully completed the first part of Project 9, which tests your understanding of the concepts covered in this project, complete the following experiments. The final step is to create and print your program.

<table>
<tr><td>**EXPERIMENT**
9.1</td><td></td></tr>
</table>

FORWARD/REVERSE AND LOW-HIGH

Name _____   Date _____

Approved by _____

Purpose

Convert the relay control circuit shown in figure 9.3 to a PLC program. This circuit controls a three-phase, two-speed separate winding motor. The circuit operates as follows:

1. A stop and a forward/reverse pushbutton controls the direction of the motor.
2. A single-pole toggle switch controls the selection of the low and high speed of the motor.

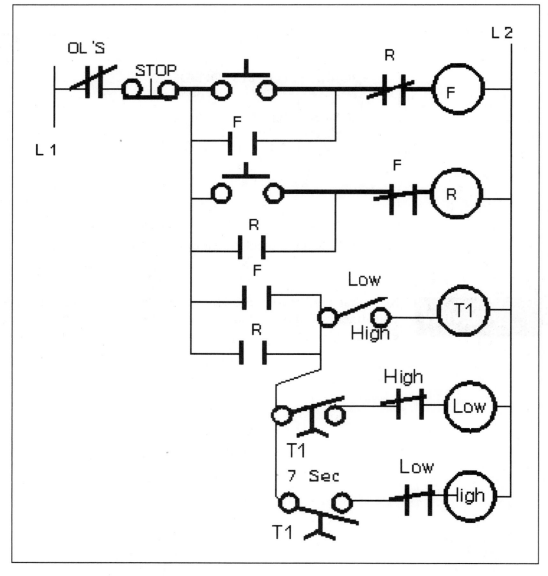

Figure 9.3. Forward/Reverse Low-High Circuit.

3. Pressing either the forward or reverse pushbuttons always starts the motor in low. When selecting the low speed, the motor starts and remains in low
4. Selecting the high speed motor starts in low. After a preset time, it automatically goes to high.
5. Place the jump to label zone shown below in figure 9.4 around this experiment.
6. Use the same timer address as the timer in the project. The purpose is to test your jump to label instructions. When you have completed the previous procedures, run the circuit and verify the jump to label instruction. Toggle switch (00) will control Project 9 or Experiment 9.1. When this program is in operation, the program in Project 9 will not function.

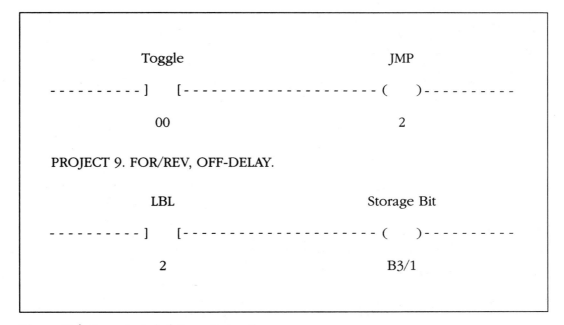

Figure 9.4. Jump to Label Zone Instructions.

UP/DOWN COUNTER

OBJECTIVES

Purpose: To develop a program using an Up/Dn counter instruction for counting and rejecting the total number of parts in a process system.

After completion of this project, you should be able to:
- Understand the concept of Up/Dn counters.
- Understand and use comparison instructions.
- Use an integer to BCD instruction (TOD).

REFERENCE READING

To preview an example and a brief description of each instruction that will be used in this project, refer to Appendix A: Timer/Counter, Compare and Conversion Instructions. CTU, CTD, RES, TON, RTO, EQU, LEQ, LES, TOD.

DISCUSSION

Down-counter instruction can be paired to an up-counter instruction to form an Up/Dn counter. Unless the program logic is used to prevent up-counters from exceeding their preset value, they will continue counting past the preset value. Using a normally closed done bit (C5:1.DN) in the up-counter rung prevents the counter from exceeding its preset value. See figure 10.1.

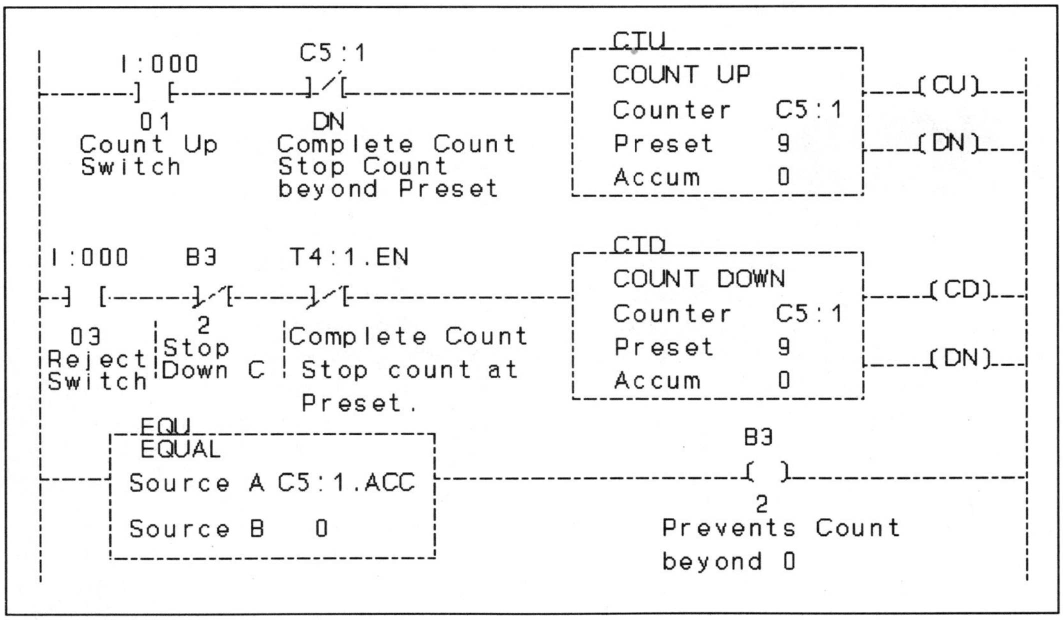

Figure 10.1 Up-Down Counter Program.

To stop the down count from underflowing past zero accumulated value, a normally closed storage bit (B3/2) is used. A separate rung with an equal-to-zero input instruction activates the output storage bit (B3/2) to stop the down count at zero. Another bit (T4:1.EN) is used in the down count to prevent any further down counting when the up count accumulated value is equal to the preset value

Project

In this project, you will be programming an Up/Dn counter that will be used to count the number of good parts with an up-counter. The down-counter will reduce the count when a flawed part is rejected.

Two timers are also used in the circuit:
1. The first is a timer-on delay used to reset the system when the count is complete. The timer will delay the reset for a preset time.
2. The second is a retentive timer to activate an alarm if the counter has exceeded the preset time of the timer. The preset number of good parts must be completed within a preset time frame.

PROGRAM LOGIC

1. A CTU instruction to count the number of parts completed by the process.
2. A CTD instruction to count the number of parts rejected.
3. An equal instruction to prevent down count underflowing beyond zero.
4. A TON to reset the process after five seconds.
5. A retentive timer to keep track of the time involved in the making of the good parts. A greater than or equal instruction (GEQ) to control the retentive timer.
6. An alarm warning of too much time in the completion of the parts.
7. The following is the sequence of events.
   A. An up-counter that counts nine completed parts and a down counter that counts down any rejects.
   B. After nine completed parts, the system stops for five seconds and resets.
   C. A retentive timer to turn on an alarm if too much time is exceeded in the process of the completed parts.

PROCEDURES

1. Enter the program on the PLC for the Up/Dn circuit as shown in figure 10.1. The purpose of the first portion of this project is to investigate and verify the operation of the Up/Dn counters.
2. Turn to the run mode and check your circuit. You should be able to count up to the preset of nine and not beyond this number. Next try counting down to zero. Your program should not allow you to go beyond zero.
3. Next, enter the following rungs described in the steps listed below:
   A. For your next rung, enter an input instruction (C5:1.DN) to control a timer-on delay (T4:1). Preset the timer for five seconds.
   B. Now enter a greater than or equal (GEQ) instruction to control a retentive timer (T4:2).
   C. Use the timer done bit (T4:1.DN) to reset the counter and retentive timer. Program also a manual reset with this rung.
   D. The retentive timer done bit (T4:2) is used to activate an alarm.
   E. When completed, the second part of your program should look like figure 10.2.

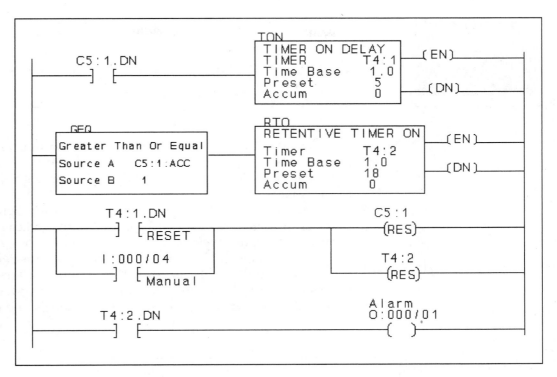

Figure 10.2. Timer Program.

4. Once your program is entered, change to the run mode and proceed to test your program. Try the count-up switch. You should be able to count up to the preset value of the counter. The count-down switch should reduce your count by one every time you close or open it.

5. Notice the greater than or equal instruction. This instruction activates the retentive timer on the first count of the Up/Dn counter. The purpose is to keep track of the amount of time it takes to process the amount of parts. If much time elapses before a total count of nine, an alarm is energized.

6. The process should reset automatically when the total preset count has been reached. Observe the manual reset, this allows you to reset the system in case of a malfunction in the circuit.

7. This circuit allows you to investigate the concepts of an Up/Dn counter, timers and comparison instructions. When you have completed and tested your circuit, change to the run mode and operate your program. Enter your documentations and save your program. Have your instructor check your work.

REVIEW

Now you have successfully completed the first part of this project. To test your understanding of the concepts covered in this project, proceed to complete the experiments listed below. When you have completed the experiments, create and print your report. Have your instructor check your report.

BOTTLE COUNT 1

Name _____   Date _____

Approved by _____

You have been asked to redesign a section of an existing program in a bottling plant. Figure 10.3 is the section to redesign. Modify it to the following parameters:

1. Copy the cycle timer, paste file OSC of Experiment 8.3 to simulate the automatic bottle count.
2. Less than or equal to 11 display a flashing indicator light.
3. Between or equal to 12 to 24 display a yellow indicator light. (Hint: use a control bit from the cycle timer to flash the indicator light.)
4. Between or equal to 25 to 35 display a red indicator light.
5. When the count equals 36, stop the system for ten seconds. After the ten-second period elapses, reset and restart the system.
6. Count the total number of cases (36 bottles equals one case).

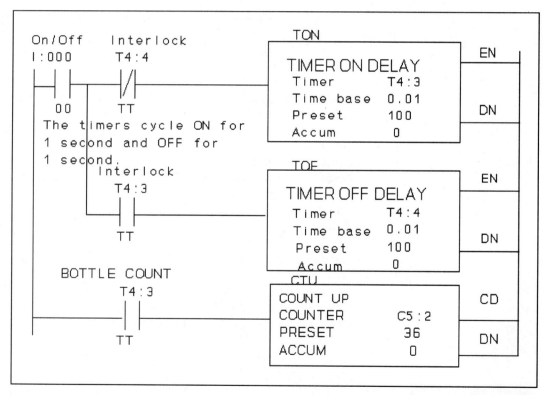

Figure 10.3. Bottle Count Program.

BOTTLE COUNT 2

EXPERIMENT
10.2

Name _____   Date _____

Approved by _____

You have done such a good job in the bottling plant that you have been asked to design and program a circuit in another part of the bottling plant. This circuit requires the following:

1. A counting system that will count single bottles and six-packs (6 bottles in one six-pack). The cycle timers can be used to simulate a bottle count. Use an up-counter to count up to 24 individual bottles. A down-counter to count once every six bottles (four six-packs).
2. Stop the system for five seconds at the down count of zero (four six-packs). Restart and repeat process after five seconds.
3. Reset and repeat. (Hint: Use a move instruction to reset the down-counter accumulated value back to its preset value of four.)
4. Display the down counter results to a seven segment display. See TOD instruction in figure 10.4. This instruction converts the binary value to a BCD value.

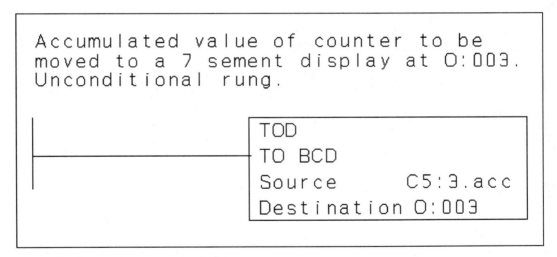

Figure 10.4. Integer to BCD Instruction.

FORWARD/REVERSE (SEQUENCE)

OBJECTIVES

Purpose: Program limit test instructions using preset time values to control the directions of a forward/reverse starter.

After completion of this project, you should be able to:
- Program window parameters using limit test instruction.
- Use timer instruction with limit test instruction.

REFERENCE READING

To preview an example and a brief description of each instruction used in this project, refer to Appendix A: Timer and Compare Instructions. TON, TOF, RTO, LIM, EQU.

DISCUSSION

Limit Test Instruction

One of the most versatile input instructions available in PLC programming is the limit test instruction. This instruction can be used in various programs where a definite range of lower and upper values are needed. The limit instruction can be referred to as a window instruction (a lower and upper limit value). There are two basic methods of programming the limit test instruction. The first method is to create a window that would make the rung true within the lower and higher limits values. This is accomplished by entering a smaller number in the low limit and the larger number in the high limit. See figure 11.1, rung A. The limit test rung is true when the value in the timer accumulated value (T4:0.Acc) is equal to or in between the limits.

The second programming method of a limit test instruction is to enter a bigger value in the low limit as compared to the high limit value. When the test value (timer T4:1.acc) is equal to or outside the limit values, the rung will be true. See figure 11.1, rung B. The low limit is set at 10 and the high limit is set at 5. This creates a window that makes the rung false when the test value is within the limit settings.

Project

In this project, you will program a three-phase motor starter to travel in the forward direction for a preset period of time. After the preset time elapses, the motor reverses and travels in the reverse direction for a preset time. A timer on delay and two limit test instructions are used to control the forward and reverse starters. The starters operate only during the times set by the limit instruction.

Because this circuit turns ON and OFF automatically, using the real world seal-in is not appropriate for this circuit. Instead, the overload contacts of the starters are connected as an input and programmed as limits in the circuit.

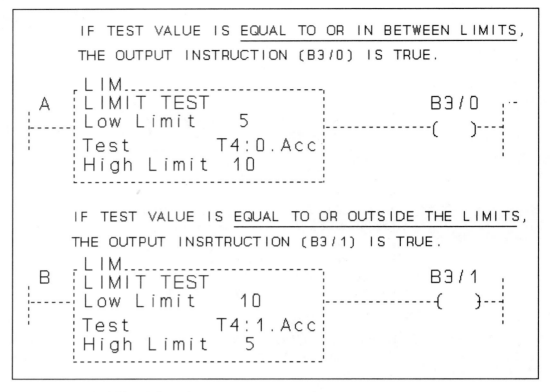

Figure 11.1. Limit Test Instructions.

Note: The concept of using a remote rack is introduced in this project. The addresses reflect the use of a remote rack number one. If no remote rack is available use the local simulator rack addresses.

PROGRAM LOGIC

1. Input instructions for the stop-start pushbuttons. Utilize bit word storage to seal in the control circuit.

   Note: Automatic circuits require a push/pull stop button to assure a safe stop.

2. An examine off input instruction for the real world overload contacts. Real world seal-ins are not being used in this circuit. Therefore the overload contacts are brought in as an input and inserted in the program in lieu of the seal-ins.

3. A retentive timer used in conjunction with limit test instructions to sequence the forward/reverse starter.

4. An output energize instruction for each of the forward and reverse starters.

5. The sequence of operation is:
   A. Forward to be ON for five seconds and OFF for three seconds.
   B. Reverse to be ON for five seconds and OFF for three seconds.
   C. This sequence repeats automatically unless stop is depressed.

6. A manual reset pushbutton to reset the timer and move the motor to a park position. Park position being the further most reverse position.

PROCEDURES

1. Develop a program on the PLC for cycling a forward/reverse starter as described in the program logic. Enter the program shown in figure 11.2 as your first two rungs.

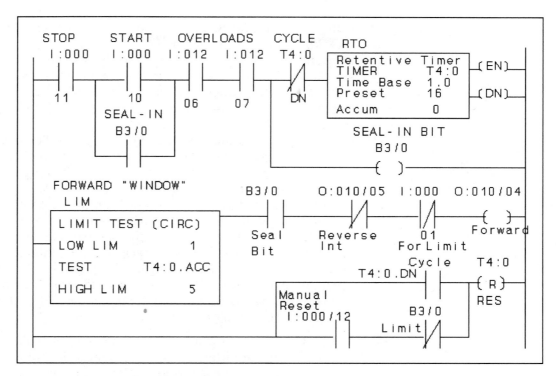

Figure 11.2. Forward Direction Program.

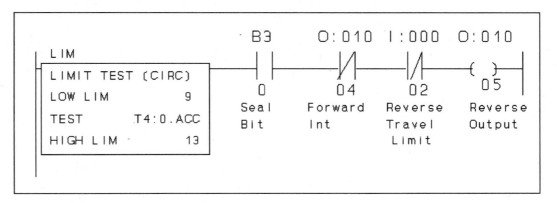

Figure 11.3. Reverse Output Rung.

Notice the limit test instruction. It is used to activate the forward starter only. When this rung is true, the motor will run for five seconds in the forward direction.

Note: Observe the addresses of the starters. The starters are connected to rack 1 of cabinet 1 for this project. Be sure to use addresses that are appropriate to your simulator.

2. The next step is to program another limit test instruction for the reverse starter (similar to forward limit rung). Use the appropriate addresses for the reverse starter and set the limit instruction window for 9 to 13 seconds. When complete, your rung should resemble the limit test rung shown in figure 11.3.

3. In the forward and reverse rungs, insert the appropriate safety limits. There should be electrical interlocks and travel limits limiting the travel distance

of the forward and reverse directions. Use toggle switches to simulate the forward and reverse travel limits.

4. Note the manual reset using a normally open momentary pushbutton. Reset can occur only after the circuit is stopped. Pressing this button would activate a reset instruction to reset the retentive timer. Provide an interlock to prevent the reset during run. Use the B3/0 seal bit to interlock the reset button.

5. Once you have completed the previous procedures, proceed to save and test your program. If everything works correctly, check with your instructor to run a program with motor starters only. If the circuit is working properly, you can connect the motor.

6. At this point, your circuit should operate in the following manner: (A) Motor should operate in the forward direction for five seconds; (B) Stop for three seconds; (C) Start again in the reverse direction for five seconds; (D) Stop for three seconds; (E) This cycle should continue.

7. Next, you may want to investigate the possibility of the overload contact opening. If this happens, your retentive timer should retain its time. When you reset the overloads and start the motor again, it will continue from where it stopped. The circuit is designed to start from where it left off.

Note: Provided it is available, implementing a braking circuit on the motor is highly applicable. You may want to include Experiments 11.1 and 11.2 with this project. The two experiments will add braking and a move to the park position to the existing program.

8. The final step is to create and print your report. Have your instructor check the completed report.

ELECTRIC BRAKE

Name _____   Date _____

Approved by _____

You have been asked to add an electric brake system to the existing forward/reverse circuit in your plant. The braking system is to stop the motor when it cycles between forward and reverse. A pilot light can be used to simulate the brake if a braking system is not available. The following are the parameters required:

Program two more window instructions to test the retentive timer of the above project. You can use equal or limit test instructions. Connect the instructions in parallel to control a timer-on delay (brake timer). Set your two equal or limit test instructions to brake at the 7 and 15 second interval.

Preset the timer for one second, with a time base of one-hundredth of a second. Use the TT control bit of a timer-on delay to activate a brake contactor coil (0:010/02).

The purpose of the timer is to vary the amount of brake time and assure that the brake contactor coil is activated only momentarily for a preset time.

<table>
<tr><td>**EXPERIMENT**
11.2</td><td></td></tr>
</table>

RESET TO PARK POSITION

Name _____   Date _____

Approved by _____

Another alteration to the above forward/reverse project is to program a reset to park position. The purpose is to brake and move the motor to a park position when the stop pushbutton is depressed, the park position being the furthermost reverse position. Use the reverse travel limit switch to brake the motor in the park position.

1. The first step is to enter the program shown in figure 11.4. A timer-off delay and a limit test instruction are used to move the motor to the park position when the stop is depressed. See figure 11.4, rungs 1.0 and 2.0. Activate the brake timer when the motor reaches the reverse travel limit. See figure 11.4, rung 3.0.

   Note: This timer is not needed if brake timer of Experiment 11.1 is used in lieu of this timer.

2. The second step is to add instructions to your program to complete the following parameters:
   A. When the existing stop pushbutton is depressed, activate the brake timer used in Experiment 11.1. Also reset the retentive timer.
   B. Program the existing manual reset button addressed to activate the reverse output. This will give you a manual, jog to park. With this, you should be able to jog the motor in reverse until it trips the reverse travel limit switch.
   C. Notice in figure 11.4, rung 2.0, the B3/1 output bit. Program this bit address with an input instruction to activate the reverse output.
   With your instructor present, test and run your program using only the starters. If the sequence of your program is correct, proceed to connect and run the motor.

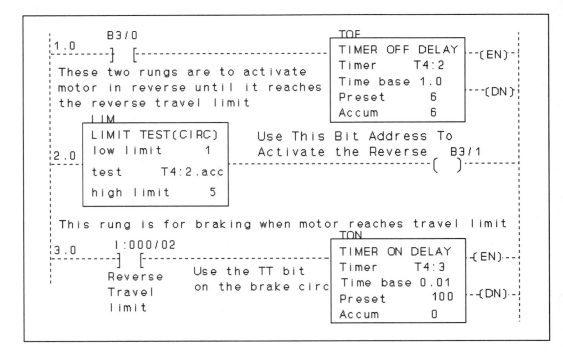

Figure 11.4. Park Program.

PRESS CYCLE

Purpose: program timer/counter instructions in conjunction with various other instructions to control a process (Chip Board Press).

After completion of this project, you should be able to:
- Investigate and use arithmetic instructions.
- Develop an understanding of floating point and integer data.
- Explore the concept of a permissive rung.

To preview an example and a brief description of each instruction that will be used in this project, refer to Appendix A: Timer/Counter, Compare, Arithmetic and Conversion Instructions. CTU, CTD, RES, CMP, EQU, LES, LIM, ADD, DIV, MUL, CPT, TOD

The processor supports and operates on two data files that are used for arithmetic operations. The first is the integer file, addressed as N7:0 to 999. The integer file uses a one-word element of 16 bits. The range of values that can be stored in the integer word element is –32,768 to +32,767. Integer files store whole numbers only. The processor will round the values equal to or greater than 0.5 to the next whole number and will drop values less than 0.5.

The second is the floating point file, addressed as F8:0 to 999. The floating point file uses a two-word element, 32 bit number. The range of values that can be stored in the floating point word element is $\pm 1.1754944e^{-38}$ to $\pm 3.4028237e^{.+38}$ Floating point files will store whole numbers or fractional numbers.

You may mix integer and floating point values if the result of the operation does not exceed the range and whole number of the integer value. Accuracy may be lost when converting from one to the other. See figure 12.1 a compute instruction utilizing integer and floating point values.

ASCII and BCD are used for display purposes, only. The processor interprets them as integers. Use the compute instruction (TOD) to convert integer to BCD if you want to display BCD values to a 7-segment display external to the processor.

Project

This program involves the use of various instructions that you have learned in the previous labs. The task is to program a control circuit for converting loose chips to pressboards. Loose chips are moved on a feed conveyor and stop adjacent to a hydraulic press. Once the chips are in place, they can be moved into position for pressing. After the press is complete, the boards are ejected onto a stack conveyor. When four pressboards are accumulated they need to be moved down for cutting and further processing. The process is illustrated in figure 12.2.

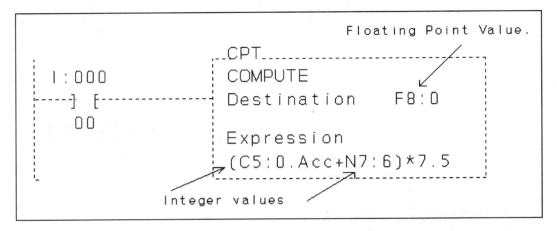

Figure 12.1. Compute Instructions.

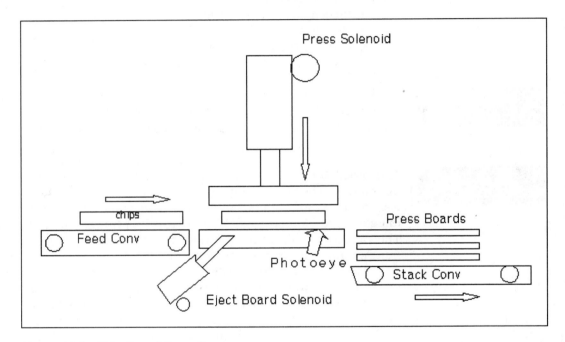

Figure 12.2. Chip-Board Press System.

The following is the sequence of events:
1. A feed conveyor is started and runs for three seconds to move the chips into the press area.
2. When the feed conveyor is completed, the press solenoid is activated for a six second press time.
3. When the press is completed, an eject solenoid is activated for one second to clear the board out of the press area.
4. Boards are ejected on a stack conveyor. After four boards are accumulated on the stack conveyor, the boards move out to be process further. Time to move boards is four seconds.

In programming, at times, one is confronted with various limit conditions that have to be met before an outcome can be achieved. To accomplish this, a permissive rung can be programmed with all the limits. When all the limits are satisfied, a permissive bit will be activated. This permissive bit can be used throughout the

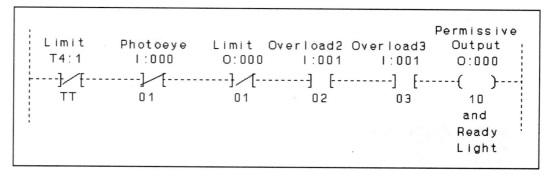

Figure 12.3. Permissive Rung.

program. See figure 12.3—this is a permissive rung used in the program. In this example, an output bit is used instead of an internal bit. The purpose is to gain a ready indicator light.

PROCEDURES

1. You have been hired to design and program a circuit for a press in a chip board plant. The process is shown in figure 12.2 and described in the program logic. Use the logic trainer to simulate the project.

   Note: An example circuit is available upon request to the instructor.

   This project has flexibility in the design. You may prefer to design your own circuit or use the example circuit as a guide to complete your program.

2. To begin, program a jump to label instruction. This will allow you to jump over this project.

3. For your next rung, use a toggle switch to activate an MCR instruction. A stop-start circuit can be used to initially start the feed conveyor and the process. Use the same address for the stop button and the MCR toggle switch.

4. The first step is a feed conveyor activated by timer #1 to move loose chips into press. Three seconds are needed to move chips in press.

   Chips should not be moved in until the following limit conditions have been met:
   A. Press is on the OFF cycle.
   B. Chip board has been ejected.
   C. Photo-eye one is clear (no board in press).
   D. Overloads contacts are not tripped open. See permissive rung, figure 12.3.

5. The next step is timer #2 that can be used to activate the press solenoid. Press time is six seconds. An output instruction is needed for the press solenoid. Use lights for simulating the press solenoid. When the timer activating the press solenoid is OFF, the press hydraulic cylinder retracts to a neutral position.

6. After the press is complete, timer #3 can be used to activate an output instruction for the eject solenoid. Eject time is one second. Eject only on the OFF cycle of the press solenoid.

   Note: Once the eject timer is complete, the feed conveyor automatically restarts and the process repeats.

7. Finally, timer #4 is used to activate the stack conveyor. The amount of time to move and clear the stack of finished boards is four seconds. Move the conveyor only when the number of finished boards are equal to the count of four. Reset the counter and wait for four more boards. Visual display on the seven-segment display the resultant count of the integer file.

8. After you have completed and tested your circuit, check with your instructor to verify if your program meets the conditions that are outlined on the project. Once you have completed the program, continue to test and run it. Follow the sequence as described in the program logic. Have your instructor check your work.

REVIEW   Now that you have successfully completed the first part of this project, test your understanding of the concepts covered by completing the following experiments. When completed, save your work and print your program.

EXPERIMENT 12.1

TEMPERATURE CONVERSION

Name _____   Date _____

Approved by _____

The objective is to convert a recorded Celsius temperature value to a Fahrenheit value and to use the Fahrenheit value in a control situation. This will require arithmetic instructions and comparison instructions.

The following are the required parameters necessary to complete the job:

1. Use a counter-up accumulated value to simulate a thermocouple input which measures the Celsius value. (Counter accumulated value = Celsius value.) Enter a counter-down with the same address as the counter-up to lower the Celsius value.

2. The cycle timer circuit in your paste file or manual switches can be used to step the counters up or down.

3. Program arithmetic instructions necessary to derive the formula for conversion of Celsius to Fahrenheit:

$$F = \frac{9}{5} C + 32.$$

Display the Fahrenheit results on the seven-segment display. For your arithmetic instruction use either integer of floating point files. Start the addressing of any integer values in files beginning at N7:20.

4. Program comparison instructions to perform the following: When the Fahrenheit value is greater than or equal to 214°F, lower the temperature to 178°F. When the Fahrenheit value is less than or equal to 178°F, raise the temperature to 214°F.

Use these comparison instructions to control the Up/Dn counters for lowering and raising the Celsius temperature value. When completed, change to the run mode and try your program. Your temperature should cycle between 178 to 214 degrees Fahrenheit.

**EXPERIMENT
12.2**

BARBECUE SAUCE

Name _____ Date _____

Approved by _____

Two ingredients needed in your barbecue sauce recipe are 3 gallons of vinegar and 3 gallons of corn syrup. Both ingredients are pumped into a mixing vat. See figure 12.4. Program the circuit to meet the following parameters:

1. Each gallon of vinegar and corn syrup requires five seconds of pump time. Use a counter to count the number of gallons.
2. When three gallons of vinegar and three gallons of corn syrup are in the mixing vat, turn on the mixer. Mix for 30 minutes (30 seconds) while other miscellaneous ingredients are added to the mixture.
3. While these ingredients are being mixed, add ten gallons of tomato sauce. Each gallon of tomato sauce requires one second of pump time. When completed, manually discharge the mixed ingredients and reset the system.

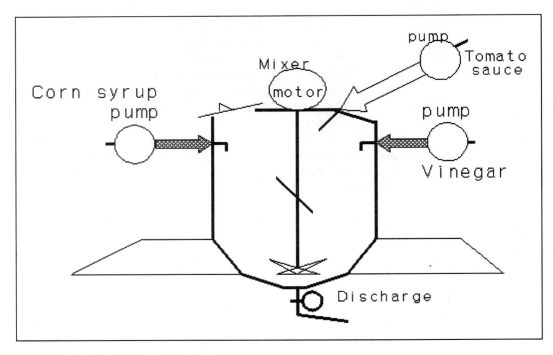

Figure 12.4. Barbecue Sauce Process.

THUMBWHEEL

Purpose: Program a block transfer read instruction in the control of an external thumbwheel switch.

After completion of this project, you should be able to:
- Understand the concept of block transfer read.
- Utilize real world thumbwheel switches.
- Use a timer ON and OFF delay in the same program.
- Utilize a multiplexer module to control thumbwheel switches.

To preview an example and a brief description of each instruction that will be used in this project, refer to Appendix A: Timer, Conversion, and Block Transfer Instructions. TON, TOF, FRD, BTR.

Thumbwheel Switches

Thumbwheel switches are very useful devices in the programming of control circuits. They can be used to input a one to four digit decimal number from the real world to the processor. This number can be used to change preset values of timers, counters, or as an integer for a process.

A decimel number displayed on a single thumbwheel switch section produces an output of four digits, either in BCD or HEX number. For example, a single BCD thumbwheel switch section with a decimal 9 showing would produce at its terminal output a 1001 BCD number.

Individual thumbwheel switch sections can be grouped together to form a multisection thumbwheel switch. Figure 13.1 shows four sections grouped together to form a four-digit thumbwheel switch. When you connect a four digit thumbwheel switch to an input module, each number of the thumbwheel requires four inputs plus a common. As a result, a four-digit thumbwheel would require sixteen input connections plus a common.

Another method of connecting a thumbwheel switch is to use a multiplexer input module. This module is an intelligent module that reads and multiplexes the information from the thumbwheel switches to the processor. The advantages are: (1) When several four digit thumbwheel switches are required, a multiplexer module can be used to reduce the amount of input connections. (2) The amount of spaces needed in the chassis is also reduced. (3) A multiplexer module can handle up to four, four-digit thumbwheel switches. Thumbwheel switch connections are shown in the instructors guide listed under the do it yourself simulator.

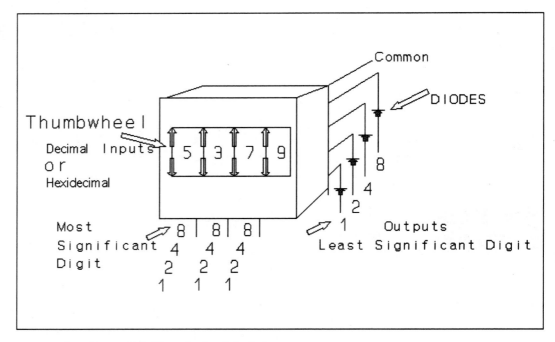

Figure 13.1. Four Digit Thumbwheel Switch.

Block Transfer Instruction

Block transfer refers to a set of instructions and a programming technique used to transfer many words of data in one I/O scan. Block transfer can performed as a read, write or bidirectional operation, depending on the intelligent module used. An input module uses the read operation, an output module uses the write operation and a bidirectional module uses both the read/write operation.

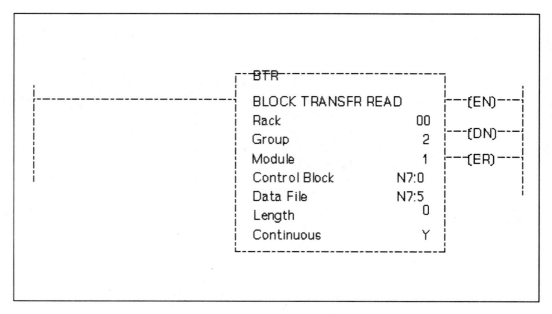

Figure 13.2. Block Transfer Read Instruction for Multiplexer Module.

In this project an intelligent multiplexer module is used to read the data from the thumbwheel switches. A block transfer read instruction is used to read and communicate this data from the multiplexer module to the processor. In figure 13.2, a block transfer read instruction is set up in the continuous mode to establish a continuous read of the multiplexer module (thumbwheel switches).

Project

This is a two part project. First you will use a block transfer read instruction to communicate with a multiplexer module. This will give you the capability of using two thumbwheel switches to vary the preset value of the timers in your program. Secondly, you will program a timing circuit to control the ON/OFF action of a switch. A timer on delay and timer off delay is used to control a minimun amount of time the starter stays ON or OFF. See figure 4.5, Experiment 4.4, Timed Switch Circuit.

PROGRAM LOGIC

1. An unconditional rung with a block transfer read instruction to read the values of the thumbwheel switches. This is used only with an intelligent module, such as the multiplexer module, to read the thumbwheel switch.
2. A pressure switch (s.p. toggle switch can be used to replace pressure switch) to activate an output instruction for a motor starter (output light can be used to simulate starter) turning ON and OFF automatically.
3. A timer-on delay to assure the starter will remain ON after the initial start for a minimum period of time (three seconds minimum time).
4. A timer-off delay to assure the starter will remain OFF for a minimum period of time (three seconds minimum time) after the circuit is stopped.
5. A four digit thumbwheel switch to change the preset value of the timers. An FRD instruction to convert the BCD value to an integer value.

PROCEDURES

Part 1

1. The first part of this project requires you to program the block transfer and write instruction as shown in figure 13.2. When you have completed this, change to the run mode. Change your screen to data monitor menu. In the data monitor menu, view the binary bits of N7:6, N7:7, N7:8, and N7:9. These integer files represent the addresses of the four 4-digit thumbwheel switches.

   Observe that every time you turn the digits of the thumbwheels it changes the binary bits on the screen. Rotate to a number on the thumbwheels and enter the BCD number from the data monitor screen in Data Table 13.1.

Table 13.1. Thumbwheel Data.

INTEGER THUMB #	BCD # THUMB #	BCD #
N7:6	9999	1111
N7:7	7777	8888
N7:8	5555	6666
N7:9	3333	4444

2. Once you have completed the first part of the project and feel confident on the thumbwheel operation, proceed to the second part of this project. Check with your instructor if you have any further questions on this operation.

Part 2

3. Part 2 requires you to convert and program the relay logic circuit in Experiment 4.5 of Project 4-Timers. This circuit implements timers to control the ON/OFF conditions of the input switch.
4. Program a thumbwheel switch to change the preset value of both timers. You should convert the output values before you manipulate them with your program. Otherwise, the processor will intepret the BCD value as an integer value. A FRD instruction is used to convert the BCD value to integer value. See figure 13.3.

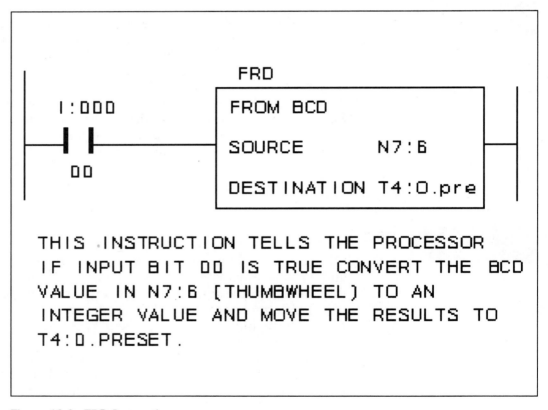

Figure 13.3. FRD Instruction.

5. When you have completed entering your program, proceed to test the input switch operation by completing the following steps:
   A. Turn the switch ON and then quickly turn it OFF. Output should stay on for preset time of timer on delay. The TON should control how long the circuit will remain ON even though the switch is turned OFF.
   B. Turn the switch OFF and then quickly ON. Output should stay OFF for preset time of timer off delay. The TOF controls how long the circuit will remain OFF regardless of switch position.

6. Change the preset time of the timer with the thumbwheels and repeat the above steps. Demonstrate your working circuit to your instructor. Remember to save and print your program.

REVIEW

Now that you have successfully completed the first part of this project, test your understanding of the concepts covered and complete the following experiments. Experiment 13.1 is an add-on integral part of this project.

FALSE STARTS

Name _____   Date _____

Approved by _____

Modify the previous Project 13 circuit with the following parameters:
1. Activate an alarm light and stop the system if more than three successive starts are attempted by the operating switch within a minimum allocated time (too many starts within a certain time frame). A manual switch is needed to reset system.
2. Use a timer and a counter to keep track of the minimum allocated time of the attempted starts of the switch. Program a second thumbwheel switch to change the minimum time of the timer.

EXPERIMENT 13.2	# TEMPERATURE CONVERSION 2

Name _____   Date _____

Approved by _____

The objectives of this experiment are:
1. To investigate advance editing features.
2. To provide a means of entering the Celsius value in your mathmatical equation with the use of a thumbwheel switch.

In Project 12, you programmed a circuit to convert Celsius values to Fahrenheit values. Begin by returning to Experiment 12.1—Temperature Conversion 1. With advance editing functions, select and copy Experiment 12.1 to your disk in a separate file called Temp.

The next step is to restore and return to Project 13. With advance editing features, copy file from the disk Temp into Project 13. After you have completed the transfer, proceed to modify the experiment with the following:
1. Delete all rungs pertaining to the counter that was used to simulate the Celsius value.
2. Program a thumbwheel switch to represent the Celsius value into your math equation. When completed, you should be able to enter a Celsius value from your thumwheel switch and this value will be converted to Fahrenheit.
3. Modify your comparison instructions to activate an indicator light when the Fahrenheit temperature is greater than 212°. Do the same for a light when the temperature is less than 180°.

MULTI-SPEED MOTOR

OBJECTIVES

Purpose: To develop a program controlling a sequential circuit using limit test instructions. After completion of this project you should be able to:
- Control the speed sequence of a multi-speed motor.
- Investigate and develop sequential programs.
- Understand the usage of limit test instruction.

REFERENCE READING

To preview an example and a brief description of each instruction that will be used in this project, refer to Appendix A: Timer/Counter and Compare Instructions. TON, CTU, LIM.

DISCUSSION

This project is done with a three-phase, four-speed, two-winding, constant horsepower motor. Realizing that a four speed motor may not be available to everyone, the programming concepts used in this project can be applied to alternative concepts. One option would be to use four motor starters or lights in lieu of a four-speed motor. Another alternative to this project, still using some of the same concepts, is to complete Experiment 14.1.

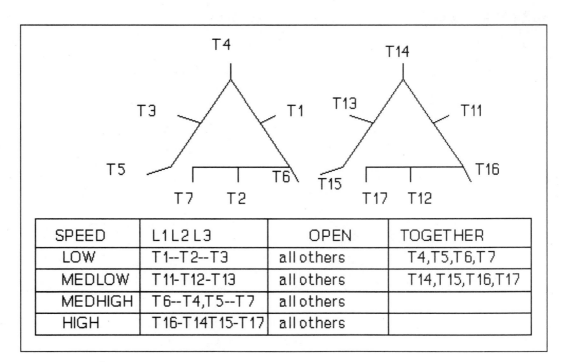

SPEED	L1 L2 L3	OPEN	TOGETHER
LOW	T1--T2--T3	all others	T4,T5,T6,T7
MEDLOW	T11-T12-T13	all others	T14,T15,T16,T17
MEDHIGH	T6--T4,T5--T7	all others	
HIGH	T16-T14T15-T17	all others	

Figure 14.1. 4-Speed 2 Winding Constant Horsepower Motor Connection.

Notice the motor connection in figure 14.1. The low speed and med-low require a starter and a contactor for each speed. The med-high and high require only a starter. Altogether there are four three-phase motor starters, and two contactors (two 2-speed starters could be used).

The project requires that the motor be programmed so that the operator can start the motor from rest to any speed. Upon starting, the motor is always compelled to sequence from low speed to its selected speed. To change speed (higher or lower), the operator has to stop the motor.

PROGRAM LOGIC

1. A normally closed master stop button for stopping in any speed. The motor has to be stopped from any speed to change speed.
2. Four normally open start buttons, low, medium-low, medium-high, high. Use the pushbuttons on the simulator.
3. Pressing any one of the four start buttons will cause the motor to always start in low speed and sequence through each succeeding speed until it has reach the selected speed.
4. Program a window for each speed. Set the limits in each window so that each speed in the sequence will remain ON for at least five seconds. When the selected speed is reached, the motor will continue to run at that speed.
5. To change speed when running (higher or lower), the motor has to be stopped.
6. Four starters and two contactors are used. Use real world seal-ins from each starter in your circuit. Make sure to interlock each speed. The starter addresses used in this project are located in remote rack #1. Use the appropriate addresses to your training station.
7. Program a separate pilot light for each speed. One pilot is located in the control cabinet the other is located on the simulator.

PROCEDURES

1. Construct a program on the PLC to control a 4-speed motor. Enter the rungs shown in figures 14.2, 14.3, and 14.4.

   NOTE: Each of the rungs that are shown in figure 14.2, 14.3, and 14.4 are the programs for the low speed only. You must program and add the other rungs with appropriate addresses that are needed for the other three speeds.

   For the first step, enter figure 14.2. The first rung identifies the cycle timer. This cycle timer cycles through the various limit test instructions to activate the various speeds. The second rung shows the stop and start rung operating a storage bit (B3/0). The start button I:000/10 turns on the storage bit B3/0. This bit seals-in the cycle timer rung. It is also used to seal-in the real-world seal-in contacts shown in figure 14.4.

   You need to program three more rungs similar to the second rung for the other three speeds.

2. Program the low speed rung in figure 14.3, plus three more rungs similar to this rung, but with different addresses. These rungs create four windows using limit test instructions. The windows determine the length of time the motor runs in each speed. The rungs are controlling four storage bits, B3/4 to B3/7. Set the limits of the four windows to the following: (A) 1 to 5; (B) 6 to 10; (C) 11 to 15; (D) 16 to 20.

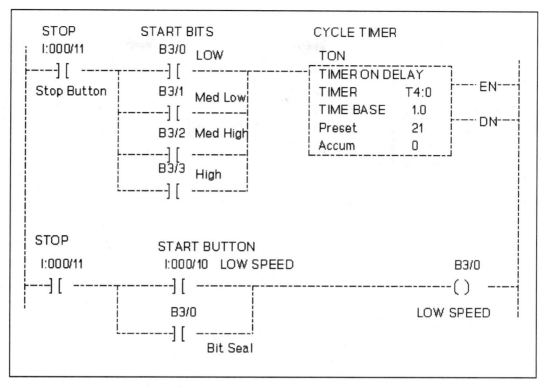

Figure 14.2. Low Speed Start Rungs.

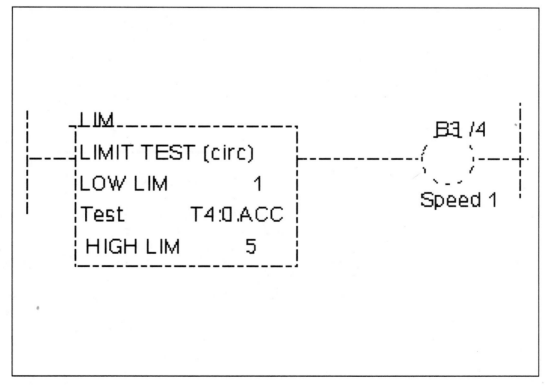

Figure 14.3. Limit Test Rung.

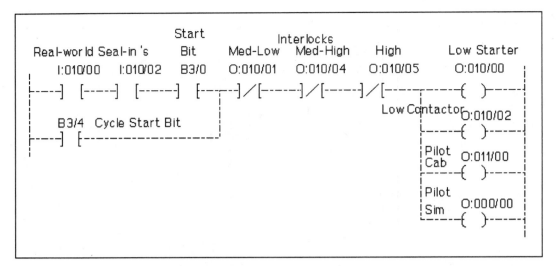

Figure 14.4. Low Speed Seal-In Rungs.

3. The rungs needed to control the real world starters are in the final step. On these four rungs, the storage bits used in previous rungs are combined with the real world seal-ins to control the starters. See figure 14.4 for the connection diagram of the low speed.
Check Table 14.1 for addresses of the other speeds.

Table 14.1. Addresses.

	CABINET SIMULATOR				
SPEED	**STARTER**	**CONTACTOR**	**SEAL-IN**	**PILOTS**	**PILOTS**
Low	O:010/00	O:010/02	I:010/00	O:011/00	O:000/00
Med Low	O:010/01	O:010/03	I:010/01	O:011/01	O:000/01
Med High	O:010/04		I:010/04	O:011/04	O:000/04
High	O:010/05		I:010/05	O:011/05	O:000/05

4. After you have completed the program, with your instructor present, check your program with motor starters only. Pressing the high pushbutton, the following sequence should occur: (A) low starter ON for five seconds then OFF; (B) med-low starter ON for five seconds then OFF; (C) med-high starter ON for five seconds then OFF; and (D) high starter ON and remains ON until stop is depressed. If everything works correctly, proceed to connect and run the motor. Try operating in the various speeds.
5. Review all the steps in this project. The function of the limit test instruction is an important concept. The concepts used in this project are important concepts that can be used in other circuits. Make sure you save your program.
6. Once you have completed the experiment, create and print your report.

REVIEW

Now that you have successfully completed the first part of Project 14, to test your understanding of the concepts covered in this project, you may want to complete optional Experiment 14.1.

SEQUENCE LIGHTS

**EXPERIMENT
14.1**

Name _____   Date _____

Approved by _____

Note: This experiment can be completed in lieu of the previous project. The purpose of the experiment is: (1) To develop a variable controlled sequence circuit. (2) To use a real-world input (thumbwheel) to the program for controlling the speed of the sequence. (3) To implement limit test, have timer and counter instructions interacting together in a working program.

Design and program a sequence circuit using limit test instructions that would operate in the following manner:

1. Eight lights to sequence in a continuous cycle. When a toggle switch operating a timer is turned ON, the lights begin to cycle.
2. At the end of every cycle the timer done bit increments a counter. The counter accumulated value will increment through every limit test instruction and activate the lights in sequence.
3. The speed of the cycling depends on the preset time of the timer. Use a thumbwheel switch to change the preset time of the timer.

The following are the programming parameters:

1. Use eight limit test instructions to operate eight output lights. All limit test to test the same counter (C5:5). The limit settings are as follows: low and high of the first would be set at one and two. The second at three and four. The third limit test at four and five, etc.
2. Program a timer-on delay to continue cycling. Set the time base of the timer to one one-hundred's of a second (0.01). Use a toggle switch to activate the timer. To start, preset your timer to 100.
3. Program the timer done bit to activate an up-counter C5:5. Preset the counter 17. Use the counter done bit to reset the counter.
4. Program a thumbwheel switch to change the preset times on the timer-on delay timer. This will allow you to speed up or slow down the sequence. An FRD instruction will have to be use to convert and move the BCD value of the thumbwheel, to the preset value of the timer.

When you have completed your program, change to the run mode and try running it. Your lights should cycle in a sequence. With your thumbwheel switch change your preset times on your timer. The cycling of the lights should slow down or speed up depending on your timer preset times.

STORAGE PROCESS

Purpose: To develop a program using a file arithmetic logic instruction (FAL) to perform a file to element and file to file logical operation on multiple words.

After completion of this project, you should be able to:
- Understand the concept of FAL instruction.
- Investigate the FSC, FLL, and COP instructions.
- Perform logic operations on multiple words.

To preview an example and a brief description of each instruction that will be used in this project, refer to Appendix A: File Instructions. FAL, FSC, FLL, COP.

Files

A file is a group of consecutive data table words used to store information. Each 16-bit element in the file can be coded with different information. This information is used to perform the operations defined by the source address and operators you write in the expression, listed in the instructions.

In the file to element example indicated in figure 15.1 each false to true transition of the rung, the processor will read one element of integer file N7:1. Starting at the element zero, it sequentially transfers the data of each element, into the destination element of O:001. The instruction writes over any data in the destination.

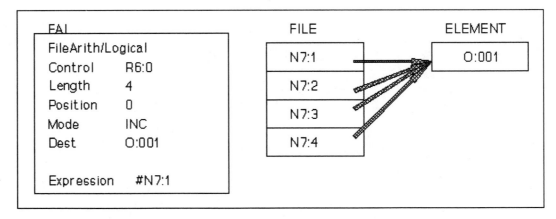

Figure 15.1. File to Element Instruction.

117

Modes of Operation

There are three modes of operation based on the rate of elements that are moved per scan.

1. The first is the ALL mode. In the ALL mode, the rate per scan is equal to the file length value. The entire file is operated upon in one scan. For example, if there are eight elements in your file, then all eight elements will be processed in one scan.
2. In the NUMERIC mode, the rate per scan is less than the file length value. The file operation will be distributed over a number of program scans. For example, if there are eight elements in your file and your rate per scan is two, then two words will will be operated upon during each scan.
3. Select the INCREMENTAL mode if you want the file operation to operate one element each time the rung goes false to true.

Project

This project uses FAL instructions to create a storage system. Information consisting of three different processes are stored in three FAL instructions. These are programmed to operate as file-to-file instructions. The storage files transfer their words of information to an operating file (file-to-element). The operating file allows the information to be distributed to real world outputs. See figure 15.2.

Notice the first rung shown in figure 15.2. This is the *operating file*. This FAL instruction is programmed to operate as a file-to-element instruction. The FAL instruction will move eight words of instructions beginning at file #N7:32 and increment one word at a time with a timer, to an output instruction word (O:000).

The second FAL instruction shown in figure 15.2. is used as a *storage file* (file-to-file). When the rung is true, this FAL will transfer eight words from file #N7:40 to file #N7:32 in one scan.

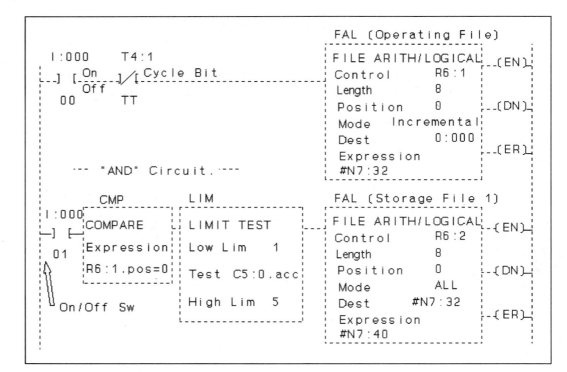

Figure 15.2. Fal Storage Process, Operating File Rungs.

The rung will not be true unless: (1) The counter ACC value is between one and five on the limit test; (2) The operating FAL control word (R6:1) is zero; (3) The input switch (I:000/01) is closed.

PROGRAM LOGIC

1. An ON/OFF switch for stopping and starting the system.
2. A TON sequencing and controlling the operating process.
3. An operating FAL instruction moving eight words of information to an output word (file-to-word) instruction, controlling indicator lights.
4. Three storage FAL instructions (file-to-file) each storing eight words of different information to operate with the following:
   A. Storage FAL's data can be moved to the operating process only when the operating FAL is at position zero.
   B. Each FAL must run in the operating file for at least five complete cycles before the process can be changed.
   C. The process can be designed to run either manually or automatically.
   D. The operating file must be completed before transfer is iniated.

PROCEDURES

1. Develop a program for storing and moving three different processes using FAL instructions. Enter the program shown in figure 15.2 as your first two rungs. When you enter a file address use the prefix (#) to denote a group of words (file). Observe the address (#N7:32) of the expression file in the operating FAL. The file address begins at N7:32 and continues in ascending order for eight words to N7:39. This address should be the same as the destination file address in the three storage FAL.
2. The next step is to program two more rungs similar to the first storage FAL. Enter the program shown in figure 15.3. This program will give you two

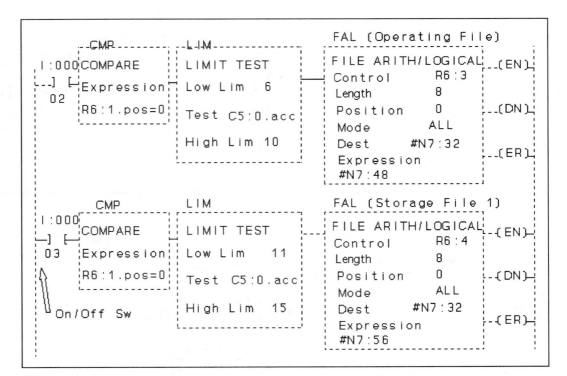

Figure 15.3. Fal Storage Process, Storage File Rungs.

more storage files. Make sure you use appropriate addresses and different input switches to control these storage files.

Observe the mode parameter of each FAL. The storage FALs use the ALL mode. This allows the complete file to move in one false to true transition.

3. Once you have entered the storage file rungs, proceed to load your storage files. Enter the data shown in Table 15.1 as your storage file processes. Load the files in the data monitor.

Table. 15.1. Storage File Data, Binary and Decimal Mode.

STORAGE FAL #1	Binary Mode				Decimal Mode
N7:40	0001	0001	0001	0001	4369
N7:41	0010	0010	0010	0010	8738
N7:42	0100	0100	0100	0100	17476
N7:43	1000	1000	1000	1000	−30584
N7:44	0001	0001	0001	0001	4369
N7:45	0010	0010	0010	0010	8738
N7:46	0100	0100	0100	0100	17476
N7:47	1000	1000	1000	1000	−30584

STORAGE FAL #2	Binary Mode				Decimal Mode
N7:48	0011	0011	0011	0011	13107
N7:49	1100	1100	1100	1100	−13108
N7:50	0111	0111	0111	0111	30583
N7:51	1000	1000	1000	1000	−30584
N7:52	1100	1100	1100	1100	−13108
N7:53	0011	0011	0011	0011	13107
N7:54	1110	1110	1110	1110	−4370
N7:55	0001	0001	0001	0001	4369

STORAGE FAL #3	Binary Mode				Decimal Mode
N7:56	1111	1111	1111	1111	−1
N7:57	0001	0001	0001	0001	4369
N7:58	1111	1111	1111	1111	−1
N7:59	1000	1000	1000	1000	−30584
N7:60	1111	1111	1111	1111	−1
N7:61	1001	1001	1001	1001	−26215
N7:62	1111	1111	1111	1111	−1
N7:63	0110	0110	0110	0110	26214

4. After you have entered the information in your files, continue to complete your program. Enter a cycle timer circuit based on the circuit in Experiment 8.3. The timers will control the cycle speed of the operating file. This will allow you to vary the speed of the information moving from the file (#N7:32) to the output element (O:000).

5. Finally, to complete the project, you need to program an up-counter that is activated by the control done bit of the operating file (R6:1.DN). Reset the counter when it reaches the count of 15. The purpose of the counter and the limit test instructions is to control the amount of times that each storage file is cycle through in an automatic mode.

6. Change to the run mode and try your program. Observe the output lights. They should be changing their sequence after five complete cycles of each storage process. When you have successfully checked and completed everything, save your program to your disk, and proceed to complete the experiments. The final step is to print your program and have it checked by your instructor.

STORAGE PROCESS #2

Name _____   Date _____

Approved by _____

Program a modified version of the previous storage Project 15 with the following:
1. Restore and rename Project 15 storage process under a different project name (Exp15_1).
2. Replace the FAL instuctions of the three storage files with the copy file (COP) instruction. Use the same file addresses.
3. Delete the three limit test instructions.
4. Delete the up-counter and its reset instruction.
5. Interlock your toggle switches to make sure only one storage file is moved at any one time. Using your toggle switches, you can manually move the COP storage files to the operating file as needed.
6. Save this program under a different project name (Exp15_1).

You should be able to copy any of the three storage processes in the operating process by selecting and closing the appropriate switch. The compare instructions allow you to copy only on position zero. If you remove the compare instructions, the copy files will activate on any position.

EXPERIMENT 15.2	# HUNGARIAN ROLL RECIPE

Name _____ Date _____

Approved by _____

You have been hired by a large bread bakery to develop a program for there new line of Hungarian rolls. The main concern is to compare a batch variable of the original roll recipe (FSC) against a working recipe (FAL) during the operation of the process. See figure 15.4, recipe flow chart.

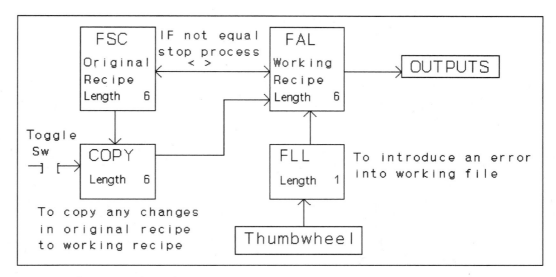

Figure 15.4. Recipe Flow Chart.

This program requires you to use a file search/compare instruction (FSC). The FSC instruction is an output instruction that compares values in source files. Element by element it compares the logical operation you specified in the expression. When the instruction finds a specified comparison is true, it sets the found bit (FD) and inhibit bit (IN). The position bit (POS) is also set to record where the comparison was found.

The following are the parameters of the job:

1. Use an FAL instruction to sequence a working recipe at an output address (file to element). The roll recipe requires a six-element file. This is similar to the operating FAL in the first project. Create a new file category (N9) in your memory status and locate the files in this new category.

2. Perform a not-equal (< >) comparison using an FSC instruction. The FSC instuction should increment simultaneously with the FAL through each element. Use a toggle switch or the cycle timers to step the FAL and FSC files. This will compare the original recipe source file (FSC) with the working source file (FAL). These two files should be equal at all times.

   Activate an alarm light and stop the process when the file elements are not equal. Program a manual reset to unlatch (U) the FSC inhibit (IN) when a not-equal condition is found.

3. Use a thumbwheel switch and a file fill (FLL) instruction to change one element in your working recipe file. This will create a difference in the work-

ing recipe as compared to the original recipe file. A copy file (COP) instruction can be used to transfer the original recipe to the working recipe file.

When complete, monitor the process with the data monitor. Your program should increment data from the FAL files to the output lights. The FSC files should monitor this operation and stop the system if a not-equal occurs in any one of the files.

CONVEYOR SYSTEM

Purpose: To develop and program a circuit for control and operation of a conveyor system.

After completion of this project you should be able to:
- Implement one-shot rising/falling instructions.
- Use photoelectric sensors (photo-eyes).
- Develop an understanding of programming conveyor systems.

To preview an example and a brief description of each instruction that will be used in this project, refer to Appendix A: Timer/Counter, Compare, and Program Control Instructions. TON, CTU, LIM, MCR, OSR, OSF.

An edge triggered one-shot instruction changes state only at a specified point of a triggering input instruction. The one-shot rising instruction changes state at the positive edge (rising edge) of the input pulse. The one-shot falling instruction changes state at the negative edge (falling edge) of the input pulse. Both are sensitive to its inputs only at the transition of the input pulse. Changes in their outputs occur only once in synchronization with the transition of the input pulses.

The one-shots can be used where a clean input pulse is needed for a reliable operation. *Bouncing* effects are especially critical when attempting to toggle a mechanical switch input.

Figure 16.1 shows the difference between a one-shot rising and a one-shot falling activated by a mechanical pushbutton I:000/01. When the pushbutton is pressed, counter C5:1 will increment one count. When the pushbutton is released, the counter C5:2 will increment one count. Using one of these instructions with mechanical inputs assures a more reliable operation.

Project—Bale Conveyor

This project is done with three conveyors, a 15-foot main conveyor with a 2 hp, 480 V three-phase motor, a 5-foot feed conveyor with a $1\frac{1}{2}$ hp motor, and a 5 foot eject conveyor with a $1\frac{1}{2}$ hp motor.

Note: Indicator lights can be used to simulate conveyors.

The programming for this project requires the delicate tuning of three-phase motor starters, photoelectric sensors and PLC instructions to interact in a conveyor process system. See figure 16.2 The project requires old bales to be placed on a feed conveyor. The feed conveyor moves the old bales to a main conveyor for processing. A photo-eye located at the front of the main conveyor determines that the bales are ready to move to the main conveyor. The main conveyor moves the bale to a rebale and repack process. When complete, the bales moves to the eject conveyor for ejecting and counting. At the same time, a new bale moves to the main conveyor to restart the process.

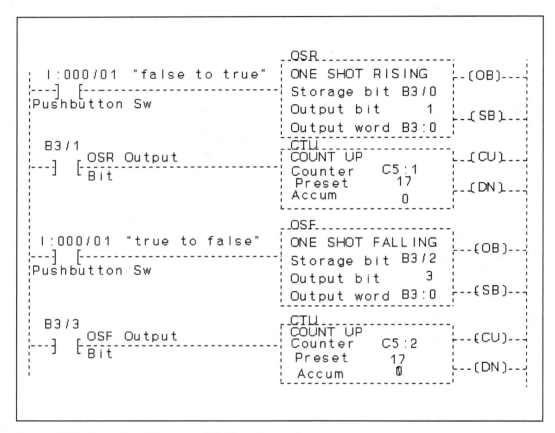

Figure 16.1. One-Shot Rising and Falling Instructions.

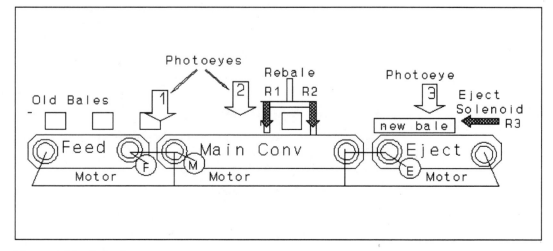

Figure 16.2. Bale Conveyor.

PROGRAM LOGIC

1. Figure 16.3 illustrates the control sequence. New bales are loaded on the feed conveyor. A new bale should be loaded every time a bale leaves the feed conveyor.
2. The feed conveyor moves the old bales to the main conveyor.
   A. Photo-eye #1 determines whether the old bale is positioned and ready to move on to the main conveyor.
   B. The feed conveyor loads a bale on the main conveyor when repack and rebale is completed.
3. The main conveyor starts and moves the bale to the repack (R1) and rebale (R2) station:
   A. Photo-eye #2, is used to stop the conveyor at the (R1) and (R2) station for seven seconds: three seconds for repack; three seconds for rebale; and one second pause.
   B. The (R1) and (R2) station is located nine feet from the feed conveyor.
4. The main conveyor restarts after the process of repacking and rebaling is completed.
   A. The completed new bale moves to the eject conveyor.
   B. Feed conveyor also starts and another old bale is moved to the main conveyor for processing.
5. The eject solenoid ejects the new bale to a load slide.
   A. Photo-eye #3 determines that the bale has reached the end of the conveyor and is ready to be ejected and counted.
   B. Eject conveyor runs continuously.

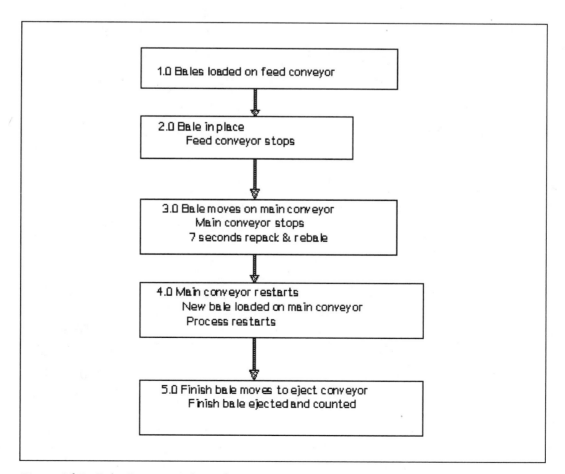

Figure 16.3. Bale Conveyor Flow Chart.

PROCEDURES

1. Program a conveyor baling system as shown in figure 16.2 and described in the program logic. Use a toggle activating an MCR instruction as your first rung.
2. The first step is to program a stop-start circuit for the feed conveyor. This circuit should be able to manually and automatically start the feed conveyor. Observe the start circuit of figure 16.4. An equal instruction is added to the circuit to restart the conveyor automatically.
3. The next step is to start the main conveyor and stop the feed conveyor when a bale reaches photo-eye #1. The photoelectric sensors are simulated using toggle switches. See figure 16.5. Observe the limit test instruction. Its purpose is to stop the main conveyor when photo-eye #2 senses the incoming bale with a delay of one second to allow the bale to pass photo-eye #2.

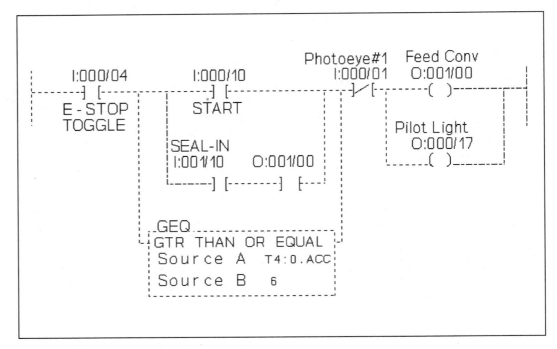

Figure 16.4. Feed Conveyor Rung.

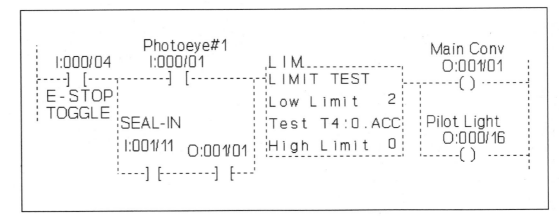

Figure 16.5. Main Conveyor Rung.

4. Program photo-eye #2 to control a timer-on delay preset for seven seconds. Use the timer TT bit to seal the timer.

5. Program two limit test instructions to test the timer accumulated value for the control of the (R1) and (R2) solenoids. The limit test instructions allow you to easily adjust the amount of time for those two solenoids. Set limits at one to three and four to six. Use output lights to simulate the repack (R1) rebale (R2).

6. The last phase of the program is the eject conveyor and solenoid. Program a stop-start circuit for the conveyor which runs continually. Use the same E-stop address as the feed and main conveyor. Photo-eye #3 activates a counter. Use the counter CU bit to activate the eject solenoid. Manually re-set the counter.

7. Once you have finished, proceed to test and run your program with your instructor present. Follow the sequence as described in the program logic. Document and save your program.

8. When you have completed the experiments, create and print your program. Have your instructor check the completed program.

REVIEW   This concludes the conveyor system project. To test your understanding of the principles covered in this project, complete the experiments.

**EXPERIMENT
16.1**

BOX CONVEYOR

Name _____   Date _____

Approved by _____

On one of the assembly conveyors in your plant, boxes sometimes get caught and pile up on the conveyor. You are asked to design and program a circuit that would trigger an alarm if this occurs. The following are the operating parameters:

1. In normal operation boxes, move past photo-eye #1 every one to three seconds. Use a stop-start circuit to start the conveyor.

2. Situation 1—When no box moves past photo-eye #1 for five seconds or more, an alarm should be activated. If longer than ten seconds, the conveyor should be stopped.

3. Situation 2—If a box should accidently be stuck in front of photo-eye #1 for more than five seconds, the alarm should be activated. If longer than ten seconds, the conveyor should be stopped. In order to re-start, a reset button has to unlatch the circuit.

4. Program limit switch #1 to count the number of boxes. Include a one-shot rising instruction to activate the counter. A one-shot rising instruction requires a PLC 5/11 or higher processor. If a processor is not available, omit the one-shot rising instruction.

PAINT SHIFT

OBJECTIVES

Purpose: To implement a shift register and a coding system for controlling an automatic painting system of pans on a chain conveyor. After completion of this project, you should be able to:
- Understand the concept of bit shift left and right.
- Implement masked move instruction to code the outputs of a shift.

REFERENCE READING

To preview an example and a brief description of each instruction that will be used in this project, refer to Appendix A: Bit Modify and Move, Bit Shift, and Program Control Instructions. MVM, BSL, BSR, OSR, OSF, ONS.

DISCUSSION

Shift registers are very important in applications involving the storage and transfer of data in a control system. The basic difference between a register and a counter is that a register has no specified sequence of states. In general, a register is used solely for storing and shifting data (ones and zeros) entered into it from an external source.

The storage capacity of a shift register is the number of ones and zeros of digital data it can retain. Each stage of a shift register represents one bit of storage capacity; therefore the number of stages determines the total storage capacity.

The shifting capability of a register permits the movement of data from stage to stage within the register or into or out of the register upon application of shift (clock) pulses. Figure 17.1 shows the types of data movement in shift register operations. The block represents any four-bit register while the arrows indicate the direction of data movement. The bit shift left instruction used in this project operates similar to the serial in parallel out movement.

Project

In this project, paint spray guns are controlled from a point outside a spray booth. See figure 17.2. A shift register signal is stored and follows each hanger carrying a pan. When these hangers reach the proper spray gun, output solenoids activate the spray gun.

An input limit switch mounted outside the spray booth is tripped when a pan is on the hanger. This enters a signal into the shift register. A shift limit switch is mounted on the conveyor so that it is tripped by each hanger, whether a pan is on the hanger or not. This switch operates to advance (clock) the pattern of signal through the shift register. The signal follows the pan along the conveyor. When the shift register signal reaches the proper stage, it activates a spray gun to apply a coat of paint. The spray gun selected is determined by a code that is entered in a masked move instruction.

131

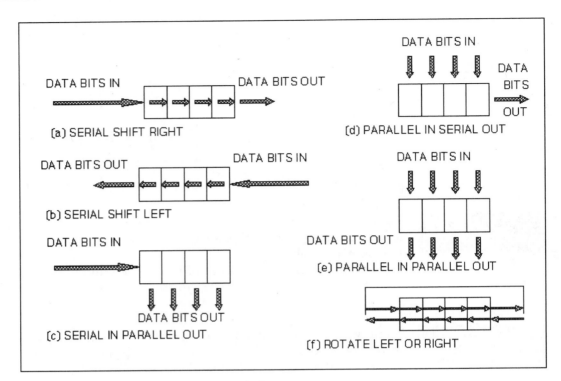

Figure 17.1. Basic Data Movement in Shift Registers.

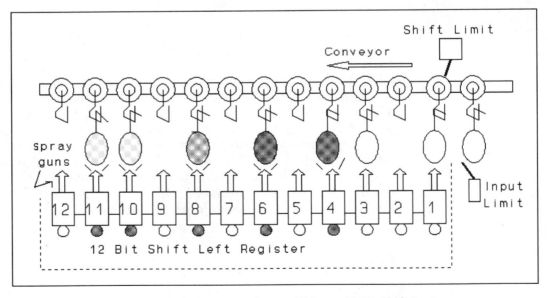

Figure 17.2. Paint Spray Booth Conveyor System Using a 12-Bit Shift Register.

PROGRAM LOGIC

1. The primary objective is to program a logic circuit using a twelve-input shift left register to control twelve paint spray guns. A stop-start pushbutton is used to start the paint spray conveyor.

2. An input limit switch is used to detect a pan on the conveyor. When a pan is detected by this switch, the rung will be true and the storage bit will be set (data bit in). Many types of sensing devices, such as photo-eyes or proximity switches, can be used to accomplish these inputs. In our case, we will use momentary push buttons to simulate the limit switches. Program the input switch with a one-shot rising instruction.

3. A shift limit switch is needed to clock the shift register instruction. Activating the rung of the shift instruction from false to true will shift the bit shift register. Program this switch with a one-shot falling instruction.

4. A masked move instruction is used to set up a coding system. The code will allow you to determine which output solenoid is functional. The output solenoids control the type and color of paint. Use a 4-bit hex code to set up which spray gun will function. Output lights can be used to simulate the paint solenoids.

5. Program a system counting the pans as they unload from the shift register.

PROCEDURES

1. Your first rung should be a toggle switch activating an MCR instruction. In the next rung, use a stop-start to control the conveyor starter. Use the toggle switch address as your stop address.

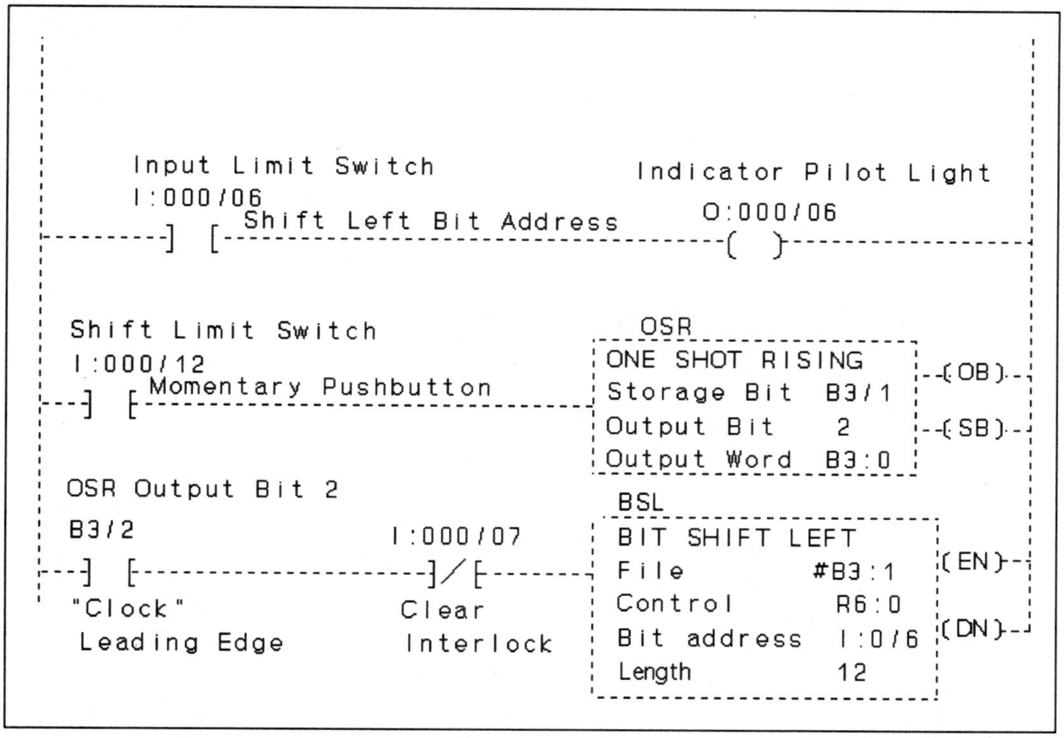

Figure 17.3. Shift Left Instruction Rungs.

2. For the next three rungs, enter the program shown in figure 17.3. The first rung consists of the input limit switch activating an indicator light and the load bit of the shift register. The next rung shows the shift limit switch activating the one-shot rising instruction. In the next rung the shift left instruction is clocked on the leading edge with the one-shot output bit.

Note: The PLC 5/10 and 5/15 do not support the OSR and OSF instructions. If you are using one of these processors, bypass the one-shot instructions and control the shift instruction directly with the switch.

3. The next step is to enter the masked move instruction shown in figure 17.4. Notice the mask address that is a hex code used to control the output bits. The code will allow only certain bits from the shift register to pass through and activate the output bits accordingly.

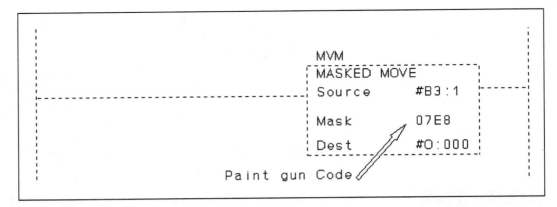

Figure 17.4. Masked Move Instruction.

4. Complete the rest of the program by adding a counter to count the pans as they unload from the shift. Preset the counter for sixteen pans. Use the unload bit (R6:0.L) and done bit (R6:0.DN) of the control word "anded" together to control the counter. Use the done bit to reset the counter.
5. Finally, on a separate rung enter a clear instruction activated by a toggle switch to clear the shift register.
6. Change to the run mode and verify the operation of the shift with the following steps:
   A. Turn on the input limit switch I:000/06 to activate an input source bit. Pilot will verify input bit activated.
   B. Press the shift limit switch I:000/12 once. This should enter the first input source bit into the shift left instruction file at the least significant number of your file (bit 32). When you keep pulsing the shift switch, it continues to move the input bit to its next adjacent location until it reaches the end of its file word. The unload bit will be set when the input bit reaches the end of its length. See figure 17.5.
7. Change to program mode and insert a different masked code. Clear the shift then repeat above steps. Output lights O:000 will be activated depending on the masked code. Compare your observations with the masked code.
8. This concludes the project on a shift register. To test your understanding of the principles covered in this project, design and program the circuits in the following experiments.

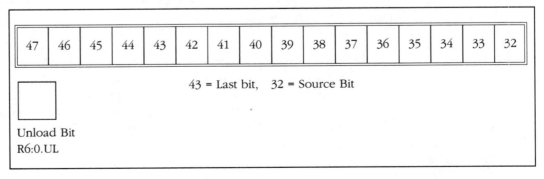

Figure 17.5. 12-Bit Shift Left Bit File.

RING SHIFT

Name _____   Date _____

Approved by _____

Design and program a control circuit to operate sixteen bits in a shift right system. Program the shift to re-circulate (wrap around) one or more bits on a continual basis. Program the shift with the folowing parameters:

1. A momentary push button to clock a one-shot rising instruction (OSR). Use the OSR output bit to clock the shift right register. Use the B3:2 file to address the shift register file.

2. A toggle switch to control an output. Address this output to the input source bit. Also, program the control file unload bit (R6:1.UL) in parallel with the toggle switch. This will reload the shift register automatically.

3. Program a toggle switch to clear the shift. Use a clear instruction.

When completed you should be able to load a bit in the shift register and continue to shift this bit until it reloads and continues to shift.

**EXPERIMENT
17.2**

Name _____   Date _____

Approved by _____

RIGHT OR LEFT SHIFT REGISTER

Design and program a control circuit to operate a sixteen-bit shift right and shift left control system. Program the shift with the following parameters:

1. A toggle switch to load the shift left instruction, and second toggle switch to load the shift right instruction. Use the B3:3 file for your shift. Do not use any one-shot rising instructions in this experiment.
2. A momentary push button to shift left and a second pushbutton to shift right. Load only one bit in the shift. Once a bit is loaded, you should be able to shift this bit in any direction.
3. Program a timer-off delay to be activated by one of the bits in the shift register.
4. Program a timer-on delay to be activated by another bit in the shift register.
5. Program a move instruction to move the B3:3 shift file to an integer file.

When completed, you should be able to load a bit into the shift register and proceed to move this bit in either direction. Observe the two timers and compare their operation. The timer-off delay begins its timing cycle when the shift bit passes by the timer control bit. The timer-on delay is activated when the shift bit stops on the location of the timer control bit.

EXPERIMENT 17.3

PARALLEL IN SERIAL OUT SHIFT

Name _____   Date _____

Approved by _____

Design and program a control circuit to operate a sixteen-bit shift left control system. Program the shift register with the following parameters:

1. Enter a sixteen-bit shift left instruction using the B3:4 file. The source bit of this shift register will not be used. Enter a bit irrelevant to the program. Do not use any one-shot rising instructions in this project.
2. Program the cycle timer circuit to clock the shift register.
3. Use a thumbwheel switch to load a sixteen-bit number into the shift left file (B3:4). Address the thumbwheel switch to load the shift file through a masked move instruction. Use a toggle switch anded with a one-shot instruction (ONS) and an equal instruction to control the masked move rung. See figure 17.6. The purpose of this rung is to load a number into the shift file when the shift file is cleared out.
4. Program the most significant bit (last bit) of your shift file to activate an output light.

When completed, you should be able to load a sixteen-bit number into the shift file with a thumbwheel switch. Then proceed to shift the number serially out of your shift.

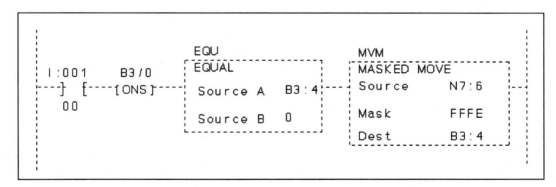

Figure 17.6. Masked Move Rungs.

LOG KICKER

Purpose: To implement a synchronous transfer (shifting) with measures of time, using compare and timer-on delay instructions.

After completion of this project, you should be able to:
- Develop a log conveyor system with log kickers.
- Investigate a shifting of measured time.

To preview an example and a brief description of each instruction that will be used in this project, refer to Appendix A: Timer/Counter and File Instructions. TON, CTU, FAL, FSC.

Data Storage and Transfer

Many times in designing circuits one has to be involved in the storage and transfer (shifting) of data. The data may represent words or bits of information, numerical values or measures of time. As you have seen in Projects 15 and 17, logic bits or word data can be stored in files and then transferred or shifted according to the logic of the program.

Another method often performed on the storage and transfer of data is the synchronous transfer (shifting) measures of time. This involves using timers and comparison instructions to transfer data from one timer to another. Figure 18.1 is a flow chart used to illustrate how data storage and transfer can be accomplished between two or more timers:

1. Timer #1 is energized when a start momentarily switch is activated to make the rung true. The timer is sealed in with its TT bit. While the first timer is running, the data is stored in its accumulator for a period of time.
2. At an appropriate time, depending on the equal instruction, the data is then transferred to a second timer #2. The data is then stored in the second timer accumulated value. Timer #1 can be re-activated to start the process again. The transfer (shift) is accomplished with the use of equal instructions. This gives flexibility to transfer the data at various lengths of time.
3. With the data transferred to the second timer accumulated value, it can activate an output or it could be transfered to timer #3 to continue the procedure. The process is similar to the bit shift instruction. The difference is in the elapse time between each shift step.

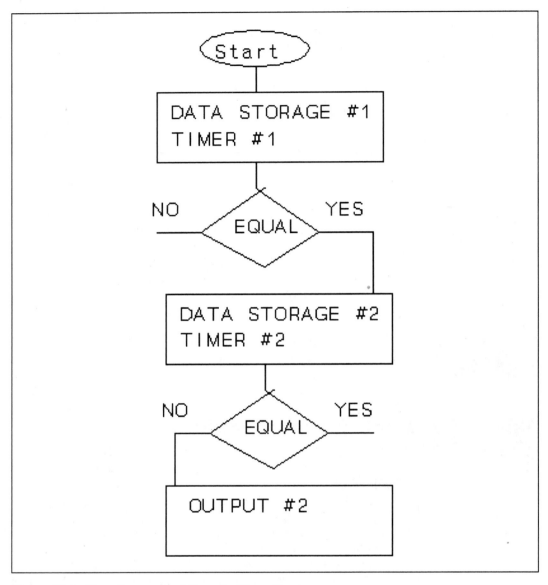

Figure 18.1. Data Storage and Transfer Flow Chart.

Project

This project requires you to program a system that moves four-foot logs along a conveyor. See figure 18.1. The logs are to be scanned to determine their size (diameter). A shifting circuit (see figure 18.3) is needed to determine the logs' location on the conveyor for kicking. According to their size, the logs would then be kicked off the conveyor in the appropriate bins. Logs will be sorted by three sizes: small, up to 14 inches; medium, 15 to 24 inches; and large, 25 inches and larger.

PROGRAM LOGIC

1. For your first rung, enter a toggle switch to control an MCR instruction. Then program a stop-start circuit to control a motor starter for the conveyor.
2. Program photoelectric eyes set to scan the size of the logs moving on the conveyor. Position the photo-eyes at an offset vertical angle from each other,

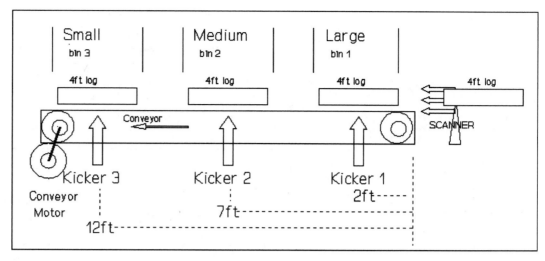

Figure 18.2. Log Conveyor Process.

large log photo-eye first, then medium, and small log last. All logs are four feet in length and the sizes are:
  A. Small, up to 14 inches in diameter, photo-eye #1.
  B. Medium, 15 to 24 inches in diameter, photo-eye #2.
  C. L arge, 25 inches and larger, photo-eye #3.
3. A kick log solenoid starter is needed for each kicker to kick log in appropriate bins.
  A. A manual override is needed for operating kickers
  B. A one-second timer is needed for kicking logs and retracting kickers.
4. A memory circuit is needed to determine the size of the logs on the conveyor. A maximum of three logs can ride the conveyor at any one time, with the following combinations possible:
  A. Small logs = three log maximum
  B. Medium logs = two log maximum
  C. Large logs = one log maximum
  D. any mix of above sizes
5. Sequence of operation will include the following steps:
  A. Photo-eyes scan the logs for size on entry.
  B. Conveyor operates at one second per foot.
  C. Bin locations on center are: large, two feet; medium, seven feet; and small twelve feet, all measured on centers from point of entry.
  D. Logs always have approximately one foot of space between each other.
  E. Any log that is not kicked for any reason will continue in a loop to be reentered and kicked.

PROCEDURES

1. Design and program a log kicker system as illustrated in figure 18.2. This requires a data storage and shift system that would keep track of the logs on the conveyor.
2. For the first rung program, a toggle switch is needed to activate an MCR instruction. Then enter a stop-start circuit to operate a motor starter for the conveyor.
3. The next step is to enter the data memory storage program shown in figure 18.3. This is the circuit for the medium size logs. Two timers are used to keep track of two medium size logs. An equal instruction and another timer activate the medium log kicker. Pilot lights can be used to simulate the kicker.

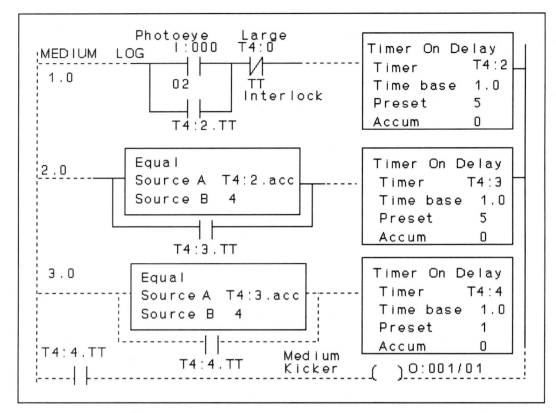

Figure 18.3. Data Storage and Transfer Rungs.

4. The memory circuit of figure 18.3 with modifications can also be used for small and large logs. Large logs would require only one timer, while small logs would require three timers to keep track of the logs. Program the memory circuit for the small and large logs and combine it with the medium circuit given in figure 18.3.

   Make sure that the first timer TT bit of the medium log interlocks out the small photo-eye. Use the TT bit of the first timer of the large log memory circuit to interlock out the photo-eye of the medium and small logs.

5. With your instructor present, check your circuit. You may need to fine tune your timers to make sure the logs get kicked at the appropriate location. Try the following combinations:

   A. Three successive small logs on the conveyor.

   B. One small, one medium, small, medium.

   C. Large , medium, medium.

If every thing seems to be operating correctly, save and document your program.

6. Now that you have successfully completed the first part of Project 18, to test your understanding of the concepts covered in this project, proceed to complete the following experiments listed.

EXPERIMENT 18.1

LOG SCANNER

Name _____   Date _____

Approved by _____

A change is being made to the above log kicker project in your plant. A beam array log scanner will be used instead of individual photo-eyes to scan the logs. The scanner produces a number in board feet proportional to the log size. Use this number to determine what bin the log would be kicked in.

The following are the parameters of the project:

1. The board feet numbers include:
   A. Small = 100 to 1440
   B. Medium = 1441 to 2880
   C. Large = 2881 and up
2. The programming instructions include:
   A. A thumbwheel switch to represent the scanner numbers.
   B. A limit test instruction to determine the sizes of the logs.
   C. Bit addresses to be controlled by the limit test instructions. Use these bit address to replace the photo-eye input addresses of the previous project.

SEQUENCER

OBJECTIVES

Purpose: To develop a program for controlling a sequential machine operation using a sequencer input and output instructions.

After completing this project, you should be able to:
- Investigate the concept of sequencer input and output instructions.
- Use COP instructions to load a sequencer process.

REFERENCE READING

To preview an example and a brief description of each instruction that will be used in this project, refer to Appendix A: Compare, File and Sequencer Instructions. LIM, EQU, FAL, FSC, COP, SQI, SQO.

DISCUSSION

Sequences are very important in applications involving consistent and repeatable operations in an automatic control system. Sequencer instructions are used in pairs to respectively monitor and control a sequential operation. See figure 19.1. The first is a sequencer input instruction (SQI). This instruction detects when a step is complete. SQI compares the conditions that you set in its file to its corresponding real world input conditions (source). It looks for a match (file = source) between the two conditions.

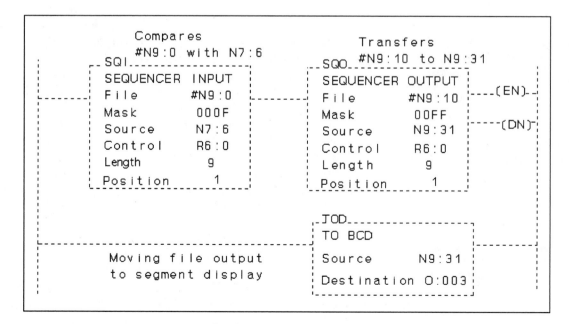

Figure 19.1. Sequencer Input and Output Rung.

When a match does occur in the SQI instruction, the second instruction a sequencer output instruction (SQO) will step to the next word in its file. SQO then transfers this next word of information, all sixteen bits of data in its file, to its destination address (real world outputs).

Project

In this project, you will use a thumbwheel switch to control the inputs of the sequencer input instruction. You will discover in this project that a sequencer input operates like a comparator. Only when there is a match between the thumbwheel switch and the input file will the sequence step ahead to its next word. As you proceed to step through the input sequence, the output sequence location will always be one step ahead of the sequencer input location. See the sequencer input/ output locations in figure 19.2. This illustrates the operation of the sequence. The sequence always starts at step 1.

Two copy files will be also be use to store different sequence processes. This is similar to the storage process of Experiment 15.1.

```
                        Steps - - - - - -

    SQI (inputs) =   0   1   2   3   4   5   6   7   8   9


    SQO (outputs) =  0   1   2   3   4   5   6   7   8   9

Step 0 is not used
```

Figure 19.2. Step Sequence.

PROGRAM LOGIC

1. An MCR instruction to turn the system ON or OFF.
2. A block transfer read instruction to access the thumbwheel switches.
3. A sequencer input instruction and a sequencer output instruction on the same rung. The sequence of operation is as follows:
   A. When the thumbwheel (source word) sees a match (equal) in the steps of the sequencer input file, it will allow the sequencer output file to move to its next word level. This will transfer the condition of that word to its destination address (output lights).
   B. Program system of using two COP instructions to store two different sequence processes. These can be used to change the file information in the sequencer input and sequencer output at the same time.

PROCEDURES

1. Design and program a sequencer machine operation using a sequencer input and output instructions. For the first step program a toggle switch to activate an MCR instruction.
2. Next program a block transfer read instruction to access your thumbwheel switches.

3. Now proceed to enter the sequencer input/output program shown in figure 19.1. Use the appropriate input/output addresses of your simulator station. Also program a TOD instruction to display the results of the sequencer output file on the 7-segment display.
4. The next step is to enter a copy file instruction (COP) to store a separate process. The process will include all the files of both the sequencer input and output files. Use a toggle switch to activate the transfer of one of these files to the sequencer input and output files. The length of this file will be the total of the input/output files (20). Now duplicate this rung with a second copy file instruction for a different process. Use appropriate addresses. The purpose is to transfer new information to the sequencer input/output files.
5. After you have completed entering the program, proceed to the data monitor and select the decimal mode. Enter the following numbers of Table 19.1 in the COP instructions of Process 1 and 2.

Table 19.1 . Sequencer Input/Output.

Address	0	1	2	3	4	5	6	7	8	9
Input				**Thumbwheel Settings**						
N9:00	0	0	0	0	0	0	0	0	0	0
Output				**Output Lights**						
N9:20	0	0	0	0	0	0	0	0	0	0
Process A				**COP File #1**						
N9:40	0	1	2	3	4	5	6	7	8	9
N9:50	0	74	32	92	56	255	256	12	99	36
Process B				**COP File #2**						
N9:60	0	1	2	3	4	5	6	7	8	9
N9:70	0	24	13	255	256	17	18	19	20	21

6. Make sure all input switches in the program are open, then change to the run mode. In data monitor, verify the loading of the information from your processes to the sequencer. Close the toggle switch controlling Process A to load it in the sequencer input/output. This will load the sequencer input and output at the same time with Process 1.
7. Proceed to step through the sequence. Observe that as you try various numbers on your thumbwheel switch, the output lights will sequence only when the inputs of the thumbwheel switch match the inputs of the file. Verify this by performing the following steps:
A. Set the thumbwheel switch to each input combination numbers listed in the sequence. These numbers will be compared to the thumbwheel switch settings, when a match is found it will step the sequence of the output ahead one word.

B. Observe that your output lights are sequencing and matching your output file as you turn your thumbwheel switch. Continue to toggle the thumbwheel switch from one to nine. When your thumbwheel reaches number nine, your sequencer output will circle back to step #1.

Observe the number 256. When you reach that number, a zero will appear on your output display. This is because number 256 in binary is located in the higher byte. Therefore it will be masked out and will not appear.

C. Stop your sequence and go to the data monitor. Then close the toggle switch (I:000/05) for copying process two in your sequencer input/output. Observe the inputs in the sequence file changing. The sequence file is now the same as the process two.

D. Repeat the above steps A and B with process two in the sequencer input/output. When complete, don't forget to save your program.

8. You should have discovered that the sequencer input can be used to compare a fixed set of inputs to real world inputs. The sequencer input instruction is basically a comparator. It compares the settings on the thumbwheel to the input file. The sequencer output steps and transfers the information in its file to real world outputs, this instruction assumes the role of transferrer of information.

REVIEW   This concludes the project on sequence input/output. To test your understanding of the principles demonstrated in this project, proceed to complete the experiments. When you have completed all the experiments, create and print your report.

CAR WASH

Name _____   Date _____

Approved by _____

You've been hired to program a car wash system. The operating sequence of the car wash is as follows:

Entrance - Soap\Water - Brushes - Rinse - wax - Dryer - Done
Limit1_____5sec_____20sec _____30sec_____40sec_____50sec_____60sec

1. Use a sequencer input and sequencer output instruction. Limit 1 will start the conveyor to move car forward. The conveyor will run for a preset amount of time (60 seconds) for each car entering the car wash. Allow for only one car in the car wash at any time.

2. The car proceeds along the conveyor and the wash functions will be activated by a sequencer output.

3. The sequencer input can be used to compare the times of the washing sequences listed above to a timer-on delay.

PROJECT 20.0

SEQUENTIAL FUNCTION CHART

OBJECTIVES

Purpose: To investigate the concept of sequential function chart (SFC) modular programming.

After completion of this project, you should be able to:
* Develop and program sequential function charts.
* Use an existing project and subdivide it into logical blocks containing only one idea or one set of action.

REFERENCE READING

To preview an example and a brief description of each instruction that will be used in this project, refer to Appendix A: Entering Step/Transition Pairs, Creating Selection and Simultaneous Branches.

DISCUSSION

A sequential function chart (SFC) lets you implement structured top down program development. Structured programming is an important concept affecting the design and organization of software.

Instead of creating a long ladder program, you can divide the program into several steps that the processor can run one at a time. Each step is related to a program file that contains the ladder logic necessary to complete the associated control task. This type of programming allows you to specify the order in which the processor runs the program files. SFC tells the processor which program file to run and when. See figure 20.1.

When you use an SFC, the processor scans only the active step in the SFC. All other steps are not scanned, therefore reducing the program scan time. As the processor monitors the SFC, the processor executes the program file associated with the active steps. The programming terminal also highlights the active steps of the SFC making it convenient for monitoring and troubleshooting problems in the ladder logic.

Project

The purpose of this project is to investigate the concept of sequential function chart programming. You will develop a simple sequential function chart to illustrate the basic concepts involved in SFC programming. The logic functions used in the sequence will be similar to the existing circuit that you developed in Project 12, press cycle. The program ladder logic will have to be modified to fit into the SFC program.

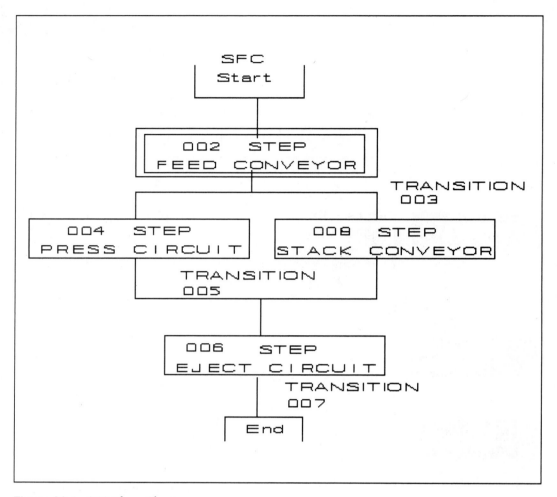

Figure 20.1. SFC Flow Chart.

PROGRAM LOGIC

1. Develop a logical, straight forward, sequential progression that relates directly to the control circuit of your Project 12.
2. Organize your Project 12 into four sequential steps. Start with the feed conveyor section as the first step. Then subdivide the remaining logic circuit into logical steps. The next logical step would be the press circuit. Continue this process until each step contains only one set of ideas, or one particular group of the process. The eject solenoid section would be the next logical step of the sequence. Finally, the stack conveyor would be the final section. See figure 20.1.

PROCEDURES

1. The first step is to construct the sequential function chart shown in figure 20.1. Place cursor on file #1 and proceed to monitor file (f8) to construct your sequential function chart. The sequence of programming steps include:
   (F3) Append Stp/Trn.
   (F6) Create file #2.
   (F10) Change file name, FEED.

(F6) Create file #3.

(F10) Change file name, FEEDONE.

(F1) Select step - cursor on File #2.

(F2) Select trans - cursor on File #3.

Enter. Use simultaneous branch and repeat above process for step #4, transitions #5 and #6.

2. The next step is to review the operation of your Project 12 press circuit. Observe how you could sub-divide the logic operation of the press circuit into four distinct sections. The logical four sections could be:

A. Feed conveyor circuit, located in step 2, transition 3.

B. Press circuit, located in step 4, transition 5.

C. Eject circuit, located in step 6, transition 7.

D. Stack conveyor circuit, located in step 8, file 8.

See figures 20.2 through 20.5.

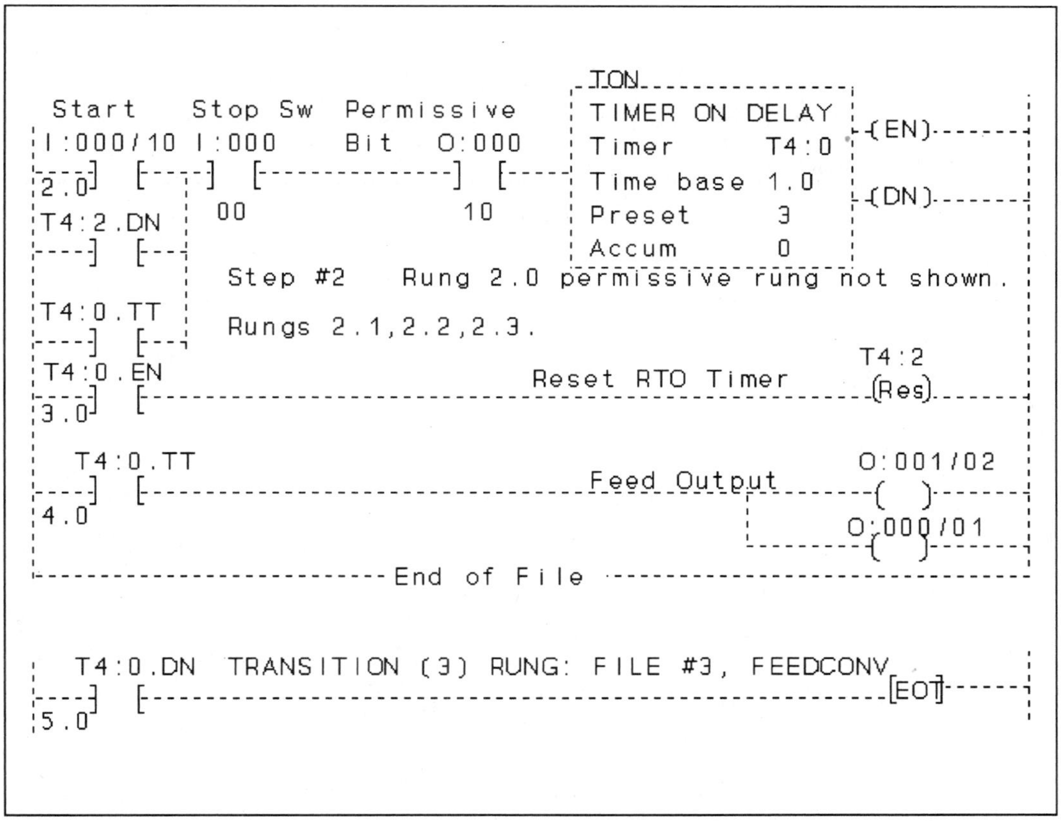

Figure 20.2. SFC Step #2, Transition #3.

Each step and transition file stores its own ladder logic. The ladder logic of a step file controls the operation associated with that step. The ladder logic of a transition file controls the progression to the next step.

With the use of advanced editing procedures, select and copy your four distinct section into past files. Then copy them into the appropriate steps of your sequential function chart.

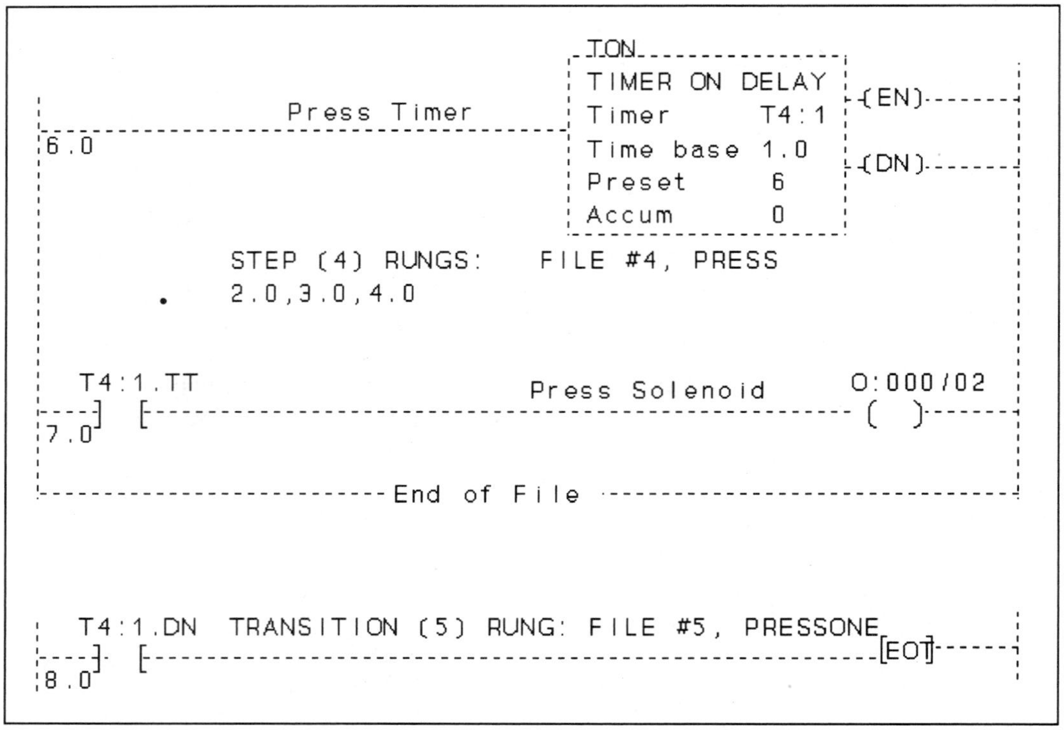

```
                                           T.ON.......................
                                         ! TIMER ON DELAY    !
                                         !                  !-(EN)----------
                    Press Timer          ! Timer      T4:1  !
  :-----------------------------------------!                  !
  !6.0                                      ! Time base  1.0  !-(DN)----------
                                         ! Preset       6  !
                                         ! Accum        0  !
                                           ......................

              STEP (4) RUNGS:     FILE #4, PRESS
         .    2.0,3.0,4.0


    T4:1.TT                        Press Solenoid        O:000/02
  :--] [-----------------------------------------------------( )-----
  !7.0
  :------------------------------ End of File ----------------------------:



  !  T4:1.DN   TRANSITION (5) RUNG: FILE #5, PRESSONE
  :---] [----------------------------------------------------------[EOT]-----
  !8.0
```

Figure 20.3. SFC Step #4, Transition #5.

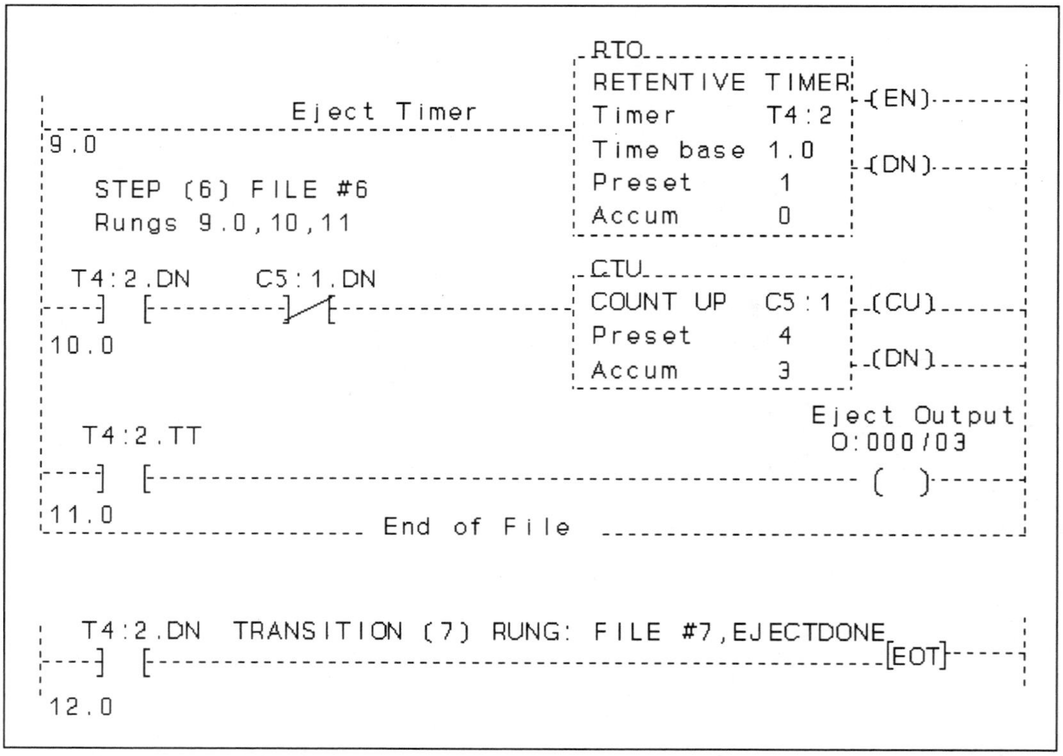

```
                                           RTO.....................
                                         ! RETENTIVE TIMER!
                                         !                !-(EN)-------
                    Eject Timer          ! Timer      T4:2!
  :-----------------------------------------!                !
  !9.0                                      ! Time base  1.0 !-(DN)-------
                                         ! Preset       1 !
      STEP (6) FILE #6                   ! Accum        0 !
      Rungs 9.0,10,11                      ....................

    T4:2.DN     C5:1.DN                    CTU...................
  :---] [------------]/[----------------------! COUNT UP    C5:1 !-(CU)-----
  !10.0                                    ! Preset       4  !
                                         ! Accum        3  !-(DN)-----
                                           ....................
                                               Eject Output
                                               O:000/03
    T4:2.TT
  :---] [-----------------------------------------------------( )------
  !11.0                        End of File ------------------------
  :-------------------------------

  !  T4:2.DN   TRANSITION (7) RUNG: FILE #7,EJECTDONE
  :---] [----------------------------------------------------------[EOT]------
  !12.0
```

Figure 20.4. SFC Step #6, Transition #7.

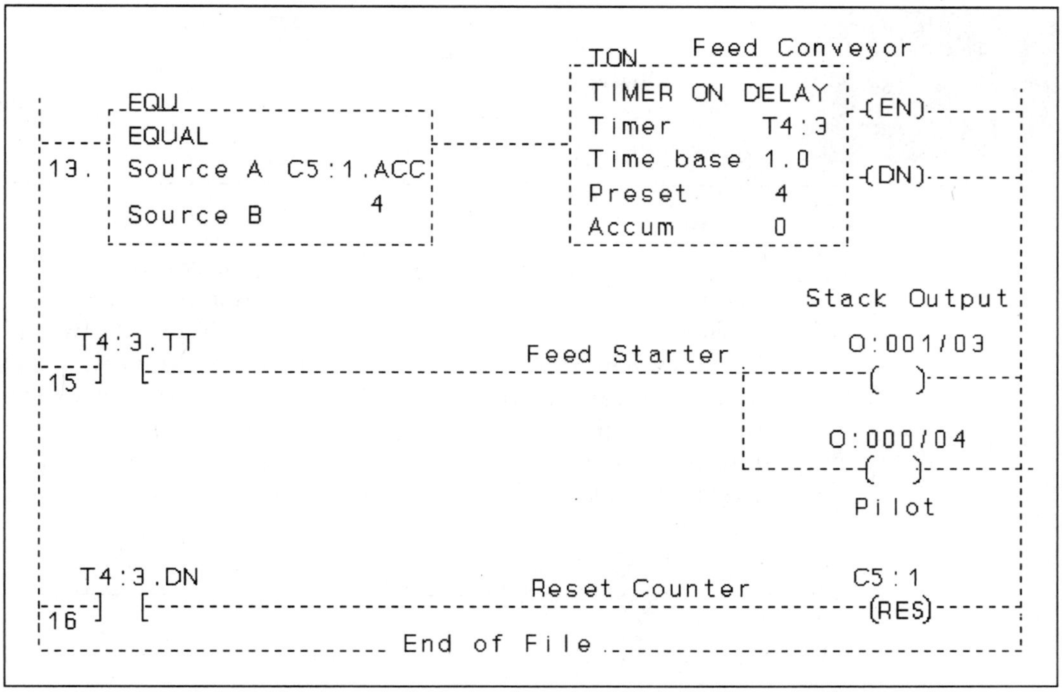

Figure 20.5. SFC Step #8, File #8.

3. When you have completed your SFC program, move to your SFC layout and proceed to check your circuit. Change to the run mode and press the start switch. Your program should sequence through each step with the following sequence: Three seconds in step 2, six seconds in steps 4 and 8, then one second in step 6. After transition 7, the sequence repeats. Have your program checked by your instructor. Document and save your program to your disk.

REVIEW

Now that you have successfully completed the first part of Project 20, to test your understanding of the concepts covered in this project, proceed to complete the experiments. Each experiment should be separately identified with rung documentation.

SFC #2

Name _____   Date _____

Approved by _____

Reconstruct and modify the SFC project that you have just completed in Project 20. Modify it to operate in a new SFC #2 layout as shown in figure 20.6. The program will remain similar to the Project 20, and only the SFC will change.

An extra step is needed for the stack conveyor transition. The stack conveyor will have to be modified to operate properly in the sequence. Use a less than (< 4) instruction along with the timer done bit to activate the EOT instruction of the stack. The less than will activate the EOT when there is less than four boards. When the boards are equal to four (= 4), the timer done bit will activate the EOT instruction.

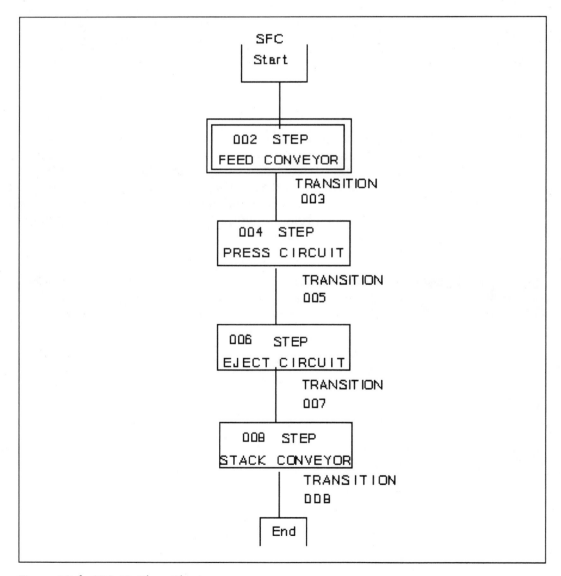

Figure 20.6. SFC #2, Flow Chart.

DIGITAL TO ANALOG CONVERSION

OBJECTIVES

Purpose: To investigate a digital to analog converter module for controlling an AC drive.

After completion of this project, you should be able to:
- Configure a digital to analog converter module (DAC).
- Implement an AC Drive for speed control of a 3-phase motor.
- Use block transfer read and write instruction.

REFERENCE READING

To preview an example and a brief description of each instruction that will be used in this project, refer to Appendix A: Block Transfer Instructions. BTR, BTW.

For further information, refer to the following publication:
Analog Output Module: User's Manual. Publication 1771-6.5.30. Allen-Bradley.

DISCUSSION

When a digital system such as a programmable controller is to be used to monitor or control a physical process, we must deal with the difference between the digital nature of the programmable controller and the analog nature of the process variables. A digital to analog converter achieves this difference between them

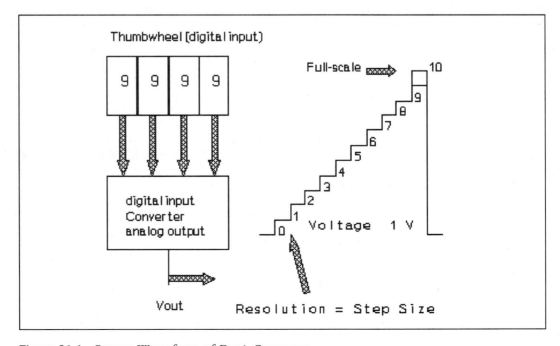

Figure 21.1. Output Wave form of DtoA Converter.

by converting a digital input signal to an analog output variable (zero to ten volts or four to twenty ma).

The resolution of a digital to analog converter (DAC) is defined as the smallest change that can occur in the analog output as a result of a change in the digital input. See figure 21.1. The resolution is always equal to the weight of the least significant bit and is also referred to as the step size. It is the amount that the voltage output will change as the digital input value is changed from one step to the next.

The process in this case is the thumbwheel switch entering a digital number in the converter and the converter processing this information based on its configuration will output an analog voltage at a certain step size.

Project

In this project, we will use a thumbwheel switch to represent a digital four bit binary code. Each binary number will represent a digital input code that specifies discrete values within a range. This digital input code will be entered into a digital to analog converter (DAC). Internally, the DAC will compare this code to its configuration and produce a desired analog output signal. We will then use this analog output to control an alternating current drive.

PROGRAM LOGIC

1. The purpose of this project is to program a circuit that will generate an analog output of zero to ten volts and operate from a thumbwheel switch.

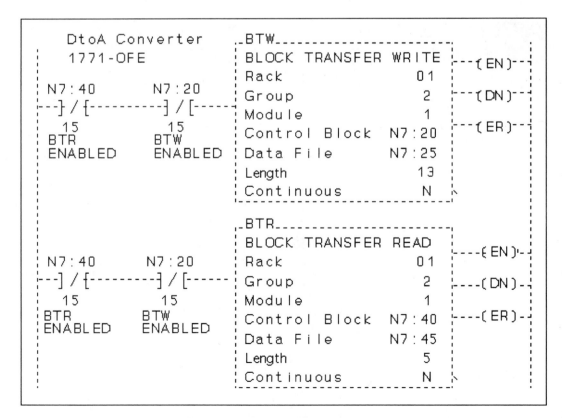

Figure 21.2. Block Transfer Read/Write for DtoA Converter.

2. Enter a block transfer read instruction addressed to the multiplexer module for reading the thumbwheel switches.
3. Program block transfer read and block transfer write instructions to activate the digital to analog converter module. See figure 21.2, Block Transfer Read/ Write.
   A. Configure the resolution of the four channels in the D/A converter module. Channels 1 and 2 are for zero to nine input. Channels 3 and 4 are for zero to 9999.
   B. Select the zero to ten volt output of the converter module to the AC drive by changing the speed select switch on the drive to the auto mode.
4. Program two move instructions, moving the thumbwheel data to the converter module block transfer write instruction (EX: N7:6 to N7:25).
5. Program eight output lights, four lights to operate with the first digit of the thumbwheel (channel 1). The next four lights to operate with the second digit of the thumbwheel (channel 2). The lights will show the BCD output of the thumbwheel switch.

PROCEDURES

1. For your first rung, enter an MCR instruction to control the program.
2. Program a block transfer read instruction for your thumbwheel switch.
3. The next step is to enter a block transfer read and write instruction for the digital to analog module. See figure 21.2.
4. Now enter two move instructions in parallel. One of the move instructions will transfer the data of the first thumbwheel to the block transfer write instruction (N7:9 to N7:25). The second move instruction will transfer the data of the second thumbwheel (N7:8 to N7:26).
5. To complete your program, enter four rungs each with an XIC instruction to control eight lights. Address the XIC instructions to the four least significant digit of each thumbwheel (EX: N7:9.0).
6. After you have completed entering the program, place the cursor on block transfer instruction of the digital to analog module and go to I/O edit (F2). This will take you to the configuration menus for various intelligent modules. Follow the flow chart illustrated in figure 21.3.
7. (A) The first menu you will see is the System Overview Menu. There, select (F6) and add a new module. (B) This will take you to the second menu I/O module type selection. Select (F10) 1771 intelligent module. (C) The next menu is the 1771 Series Analog Module Selection. The module used for this project is a D/A 1771 OFE/A module. (D) After you select the correct module, you will be prompted to enter the addresses of your block transfer instructions in the Block Transfer Control Menu. When you complete entering the addresses, accept and proceed to the Module Edit Menu. (E) In the Module Edit Menu, select the BCD option for this project. For the IFE analog to digital converter, select the binary and differential connection.
8. Select the Channel Edit Menu. There you have to configure the resolution of the module. The module can be configured from a minimun of zero to a maximun of 9999. Set one and two channels with a minimum of zero and a maximum of nine. Set channels 3 and 4 from zero to 9999.

   Change to the run mode and accept the data in the run mode. Proceed to change the digital thumbwheel inputs to the D/A module. You should be able to observe these changes in the channel menu.

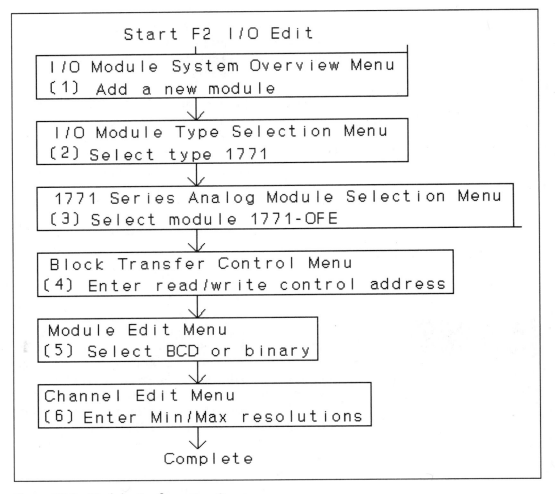

Figure 21.3. Module Configuration Steps.

9. Use a multimeter and measure the voltage at the DAC on all four channels. You should be able to read a voltage on the module in proportion to the numbers on the thumbwheel. For example, on channels 1 and 2, a number six on the thumbwheel would read 6.66 volts on the module and read 67% on the channel edit menu.

   Change the thumbwheel data and continue reading the voltages on the channels 1 and 3. Enter the voltage readings in Data Table 21.1.

   Note: Proceed to step 10.0 if an alternating current drive is available. If an alternating drive is not available, proceed to step 12.0.

10. Check with your instructor to assure that all necessary steps have been taken to meet all performance and safety requirements before turning on the AC adjustable frequency drive.

    Turn the selector switch of the drive to the manual mode. This will allow you to operate the drive with the local controls. Use the manufacturer's programming manual of your AC drive and proceed to check the parameters on the drive.

    Note: Adjust the parameters and the speed select switch according to your Project 5.

Table 21.1. Data Table.

THUMBWHEEL	CHANNEL 1	FREQUENCY	THUMBWHEEL	CHANNEL 3
0001			1111	
0002			2222	
0003			3333	
0004			4444	
0005			5555	
0006			6666	
0007			7777	
0008			8888	
0009			9999	

11. When you have completed the programming on the drive, test the various parameters by operating the drive in the manual mode. This will allow you to use local control to operate the drive and check the your various parameters.

   Having satisfactorily operated the drive in the manual mode, stop the drive and proceed to the auto mode with the speed select switch. In the auto mode you should be able to operate the drive with the DAC.

   Use your thumbwheel switch to change the output voltages of the DAC. You should be able to vary the output frequency and change the speed of the three-phase motor according to the information on the thumbwheel switch.

   Complete the following steps:
   A. Follow your thumbwheel data that you entered in Data Table 21.1.
   B. Check the output frequency of the drive, displayed on the programming display panel of the drive.
   C. Enter the readings of the output frequency data in Data Table 21.1. Compare this output frequency with the thumbwheel data. The output frequency will vary with the thumbwheel data. The amount of output frequency will depend on what you entered in the maximum frequency parameter of the drive.
   D. Save and print your program. Have your instructor check your work.

   If the drive is not operating, check the following:
   A. Measure the output of the DAC to see if you are getting a zero to ten volt output.
   B. Recheck your DAC configurations.
   C. Check the addressing of your program.
   D. Recheck the drive specifications and speed select switch.
   E. If a problem still exists, check with your instructor.

12. AC drive is not available, complete the following program:
    A. Configure channels 1 and 2 the same as the above project. Configure channels 3 and 4 of the D/A module zero to 9999.
    B. Program an Up/Dn counter circuit with a toggle switch selecting either the up or down counter. Use a cycle timer circuit to increment the counters automatically.
    C. Program a move instruction to move the accumulated value of the counter into the DAC. Use this to provide the digital input for channel 3.
    D. Program a limit test instruction to test the digital input of channel 3. Set the low limit at 1800 and the high limit at 3600. Activate a pilot light with the limit test instruction. The purpose is to step up your counter until the test value in the limit test instruction is within the limits. This will activate an output light.
    E. For channel 4, move a thumbwheel switch address to the input of the channel. Operate the digital input of channel 4 using the full value of the thumbwheel switch.
    F. Measure with a voltmeter the output of all four channels as you vary the inputs with the counter or thumbwheel switches. Enter your results in Data Table 21.2. Have your instructor verify your output readings.

Table 21.2. Data Table.

Channel	Input Value	Channel Value	Output voltage
1			
2			
3			
4			

ANALOG TO DIGITAL CONVERSION

OBJECTIVES

Purpose: To investigate the use of potentiometers in controlling an analog to digital converter module (ADC).

After completion of this project, you should be able to:
- Configure an analog to digital converter module.
- Investigate the operation of an analog to digital converter.

REFERENCE READING

To preview an example and a brief description of each instruction that will be used in this project, refer to Appendix A: Block Transfer Instructions. BTR, BTW.

For further information refer to the following publications:
Analog Output Module: User's Manual. Publication 1771-6.5.30. Allen-Bradley.
Analog Input Module: User's Manual. Publication 1771-6.5.47. Allen-Bradley

Analog to Digital

DISCUSSION

An analog to digital converter (ADC) takes an analog input voltage and, after a certain amount of time, produces a digital output code which represents the analog input. In figure 22.1, we see how the ADC continually performs conversions to digitize the analog signal at points a, b, c, d, and so on, by continuously sampling its amplitude at several points during a cycle of the signal. The result is a series of bits that define the points of the original analog signal.

A variable potentiometer with an analog output voltage is used to simulate the process variable in a control system. The potentiometer produces a variable voltage to the analog input of the analog to digital converter. The ADC converts this analog input to a digital output. This digital output consists of a number of bits that represent the value of the analog input

Project

The purpose of this project is to investigate the operation of an analog to digital converter model (ADC). To illustrate this, we will use a potentiometer to represent a variable input voltage. This analog input voltage will be entered into an analog to digital converter (ADC). Internally, the ADC will compare this to its configuration and produce a desired digital output signal. We will use this digital output to control a digital logic process.

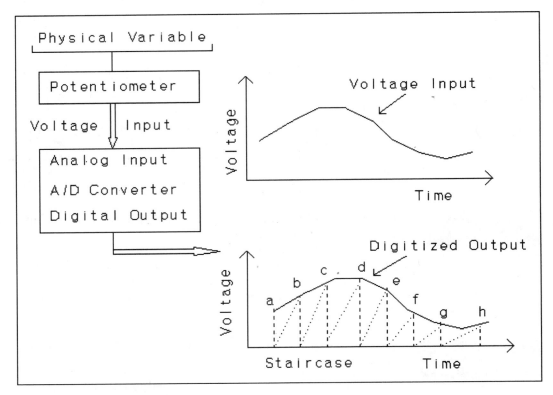

Figure 22.1. Analog Input to Digital Output.

PROGRAM LOGIC

1. Configure the ADC module for the following resolutions.
   A. Configure channel 1 with zero to 212 resolution and move the digital output channel address to the output lights.
   B. Configure channel 2 with zero to 512 resolution and move the digital output channel address to a B3:0 bit file.
   C. Configure channel 3 with zero to 1024 resolution and move the digital output channel address to a seven segment display.
   D. Configure channel 4 with zero to 2040 resolution and move the digital output channel address to a limit test instruction.
   E. Configure the remaining channels from zero to 9999.
2. Program two Move instructions, one for the first and second channel to control output lights and a binary bit file. Program a TOD instruction to transfer channel 3 to a seven segment digital display. For the last channel use a limit test instruction for testing the results of channel 4.

PROCEDURES

1. For the first two rungs, program the block transfer read and write instruction as shown in figure 22.2. Enter the proper addresses for your ADC location.
2. The next step is to program two move instructions in parallel. One of the move instructions will transfer the data of the first potentimeter to an output word (N7:99 to O:000). The second move instruction will transfer the data of the second potentiometer to a bit file (N7:100 to B3:3).
3. For the next rung, program a TOD instruction to transfer the data of the third potentiometer to a seven segment display (N7:101 to O:003).
4. Lastly, use a limit test instruction to test the results of the fourth potentiometer. Set your limits between 500 and 1500. This should complete your program. Proceed to configure the A to D converter.

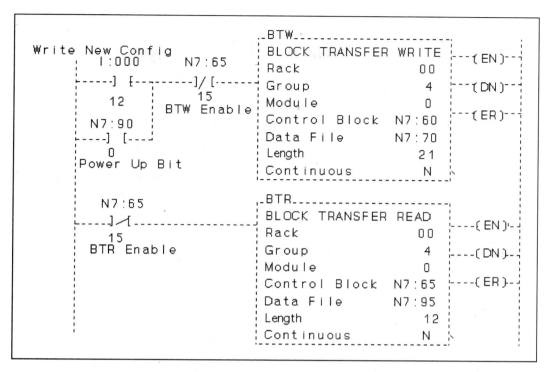

Figure 22.2. Block Transfer Read/Write for AtoD Converter.

5. The next step is to place the cursor on the analog to digital block transfer instruction and go to I/O edit (F2). Follow the flow chart illustrated in figure 21.3 of Project 21 to configure the module. The configuration for this 1771-IFE converter is similar to the 1771-OFE. Use the differential and binary mode in the menu. Varying the potentiometers will change the voltage input to each channel. Measure the input voltage on the four channels of the A/D converter using a digital voltmeter.

You should be able to read a input voltages on the module in proportion to the resolution values. For example, a voltage of 5 volts on the channel 1 input would read 212 in the module edit menu. This equals 100% of the channel 1 (N7:99) max resolution.

Vary the potentiometers and continue reading the voltages on the channels. Enter the data readings and calculate the percentages in the Data Table 22.1.

6. Observe the data in the table. The digital data increases with the increase of the maximum resolution for the same percentage output. The higher the maximum value, the higher your digital data will be for the same percentage output.

7. You should also observe and check your ladder program. The limit test instruction should activate an output light approximately between 25% and 75% of the value of channel 4. You should also be able to read on the seven segment display the BCD value of channel 3.

8. If everything checks out, have your instructor check your program. Don't forget to save and print your program. This concludes the project on Analog to Digital Conversions.

Table 22.1. Data Table.

Input Volts	Channel Data	Resolution %
2V	N7:99	
3V		
4V		
5V		
2V	N7:100	
3V		
4V		
5V		
2V	N7:101	
3V		
4V		
5V		
2V	N7:102	
3V		
4V		
5V		

<table>
<tr><td>

EXPERIMENT

22.1

</td><td>

A/D AND D/A CONVERSION

Name _____   Date _____

Approved by _____

</td></tr>
</table>

The purpose of this experiment is to combine Projects 21 and 22 into a single operating process. See figure 22.3. The final outcome will be to use the inputs (potentiometers) of the A to D converter to control the D to A converter outputs (AC drives or voltmeters). Create a separate process file and enter the block transfer read/write instructions of the DAC Project 21 and the block transfer instructions of the ADC Project 22. Program four move instructions and use them to move the digital output of the ADC to the digital input of the DAC. For example, move N7:99 of the analog input converter to N7:25 of the analog output module.

When you vary the potentiometers, the speed of the AC drives will vary. If you are using multimeters, you should be able to vary the output voltage of DAC channel outputs.

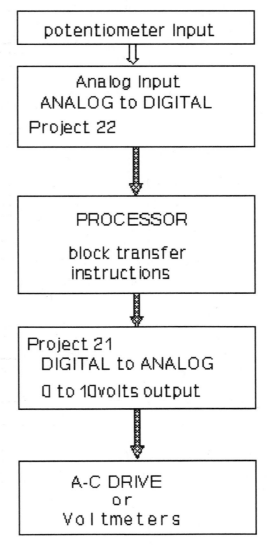

Figure 22.3. Analog to Digital and Digital to Analog Process Chart.

PID

Purpose: To investigate a PID instruction controlling a process variable at a desired set point.

After completion of this project, you should be able to:
- Configure a PID instruction.
- Configure a digital to analog module.
- Use block transfer read and write instruction.

To preview an example and a brief description of each instruction that will be used in this project, refer to Appendix A: PID and Block Transfer Instructions. PID, BTR, BTW. For further information, refer to the following publication: *PLC-5 Programming Software: Instruction Set Reference.* Publication 6200-6.4.11. Allen-Bradley.

A simple feedback control loop shown in figure 23.1 illustrates the five major elements of any feedback loop.

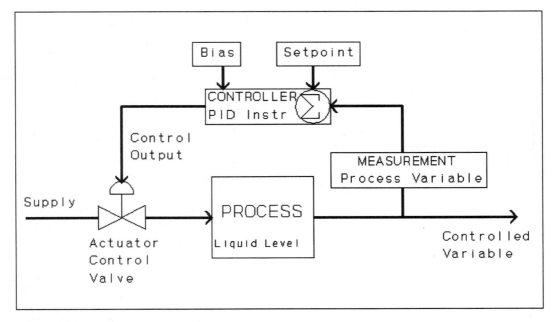

Figure 23.1. Feedback Control Loop 1.

1. *Measurement.* Data must be made to indicate the current value of the variable controlled by the loop. Common measurements include flow rate, pressure, level, and temperature. With the programmable controller PID instruction this measurement data is addressed as process variable.
2. *Set-point.* A value entered into the controller to compare the measurement signal and see whether it is above or below this setpoint value.
3. *Actuator.* This regulates the supply of energy or material to the process. It could be some kind of control valve or a motor frequency drive and many others. Or, as indicated in this project, a simple voltage reading.
4. *Process.* Ranges from a basic flow rate to complex industrial process.
5. *Controller.* Uses the difference between the set-point and the measurement signals to develop the output signal to the actuator. For proper process control the change in output from the controller must be in such a direction as to oppose any change in the measurement value. With programmable controllers this is the function of the PID instruction.

The purpose of the flow loop in figure 23.1 is to maintain a set level of fluid in the tank. As the level in the tank rises, the level detector sends a signal to the controller. The controller activates the actuator and decreases the flow rate coming in. Thus, the higher the liquid level, the more the flow will decrease. In the same way, as the level falls, the controller activates the actuator and increases the flow rate coming in. The controller performs its job by maintaining this balance at a steady rate and acting to restore this balance between supply and demand.

Project

In this project you will examine the PID instruction and its operation in a simple proportional process control flow loop design. The technique used in this project will keep the logic of the circuit to a minimal amount so as to concentrate on the functions of the PID instruction. Therefore, to represent the movement of the final actuator (control valve) an analog voltage meter will be used. A thumbwheel switch is used to represent a process variable value (measurement value). A second thumbwheel switch is used to enter the setpoint data. These two switches will allow you to manually vary the process variable and the setpoint value. Then you can observe the PID parameters and it affects on the analog voltage meter movement.

1. A digital to analog module is needed to produce a variable control output voltage. Program a block transfer read and a block transfer write instructions addressed to the digital to analog module. See Project 21, D/A Conversion.
   A. Configure the D/A module resolution for BCD zero to 4095.
   B. Connect the zero to ten volt channel 1 output of the analog output module to a voltage meter.
2. Program a PID instruction using a thumbwheel switch as the process variable input and a voltmeter as the control variable output.
3. Program a FRD and a move instruction to move thumbwheel information to the setpoint parameter of the PID instruction. Program a second thumbwheel switch. Use an FRD instruction to move this thumbwheel data to the process variable input of the PID instruction.
4. The control variable output is = gain 3 Setpoint - Process Variable + Bias

PROCEDURES

1. Develop a program using a PID instruction to control a simple proportional flow loop process. Enter the program shown in figure 23.2.
2. The next step is to configure the D/A module. Set the maximum resolution of the first and second channel to 4095 See Project 20 for module configuration procedure.

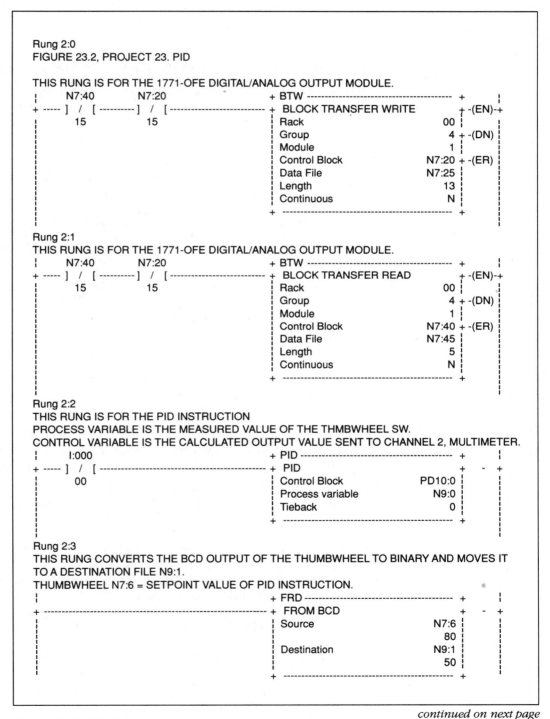

```
Rung 2:0
FIGURE 23.2, PROJECT 23. PID

THIS RUNG IS FOR THE 1771-OFE DIGITAL/ANALOG OUTPUT MODULE.
:    N7:40        N7:20                  + BTW ---------------------------------- +    :
+ ---- ] / [ ---------- ] / [ ----------------------- +  BLOCK TRANSFER WRITE        + -(EN)-+
:      15            15                  : Rack                    00 :             :
:                                        : Group                    4 + -(DN) :
:                                        : Module                   1 :
:                                        : Control Block        N7:20 + -(ER)
:                                        : Data File            N7:25 :
:                                        : Length                  13 :
:                                        : Continuous               N :
:                                        + ---------------------------------- +
:                                                                             :

Rung 2:1
THIS RUNG IS FOR THE 1771-OFE DIGITAL/ANALOG OUTPUT MODULE.
:    N7:40        N7:20                  + BTW ---------------------------------- +    :
+ ---- ] / [ ---------- ] / [ ----------------------- +  BLOCK TRANSFER READ         + -(EN)-+
:      15            15                  : Rack                    00 :             :
:                                        : Group                    4 + -(DN) :
:                                        : Module                   1 :
:                                        : Control Block        N7:40 + -(ER)
:                                        : Data File            N7:45 :
:                                        : Length                   5 :
:                                        : Continuous               N :
:                                        + ---------------------------------- +
:                                                                             :

Rung 2:2
THIS RUNG IS FOR THE PID INSTRUCTION
PROCESS VARIABLE IS THE MEASURED VALUE OF THE THMBWHEEL SW.
CONTROL VARIABLE IS THE CALCULATED OUTPUT VALUE SENT TO CHANNEL 2, MULTIMETER.
:    I:000                               + PID ---------------------------------- +    :
+ ---- ] / [ ----------------------------------------- +  PID                         + - +
:      00                                : Control Block        PD10:0 :
:                                        : Process variable       N9:0 :
:                                        : Tieback                   0 :
:                                        + ---------------------------------- +
:

Rung 2:3
THIS RUNG CONVERTS THE BCD OUTPUT OF THE THUMBWHEEL TO BINARY AND MOVES IT
TO A DESTINATION FILE N9:1.
THUMBWHEEL N7:6 = SETPOINT VALUE OF PID INSTRUCTION.
:                                        + FRD ---------------------------------- +    :
+ ----------------------------------------------------- +  FROM BCD                    + - +
:                                        : Source                 N7:6 :
:                                        :                          80 :
:                                        : Destination            N9:1 :
:                                        :                          50 :
:                                        + ---------------------------------- +
:
```

continued on next page

Figure 23.2 PID Pogram.

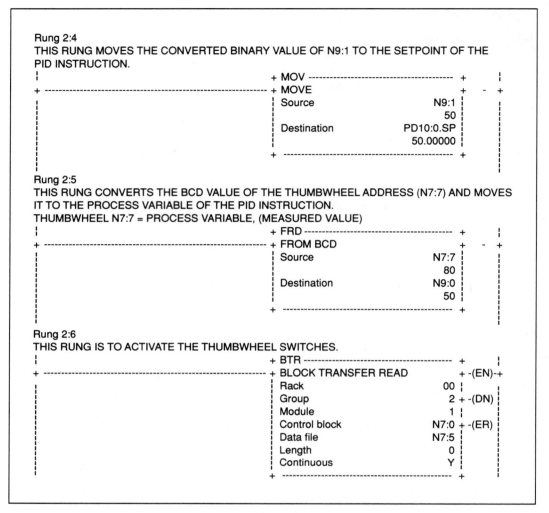

```
Rung 2:4
THIS RUNG MOVES THE CONVERTED BINARY VALUE OF N9:1 TO THE SETPOINT OF THE
PID INSTRUCTION.
 ¦                                                      + MOV ------------------------------- +    ¦
 + ------------------------------------------------------ + MOVE                                 +  -  +
 ¦                                                      ¦ Source                          N9:1 ¦    ¦
 ¦                                                      ¦                                   50 ¦    ¦
 ¦                                                      ¦ Destination                 PD10:0.SP ¦    ¦
 ¦                                                      ¦                             50.00000 ¦    ¦
 ¦                                                      + ------------------------------------ +    ¦
 ¦
Rung 2:5
THIS RUNG CONVERTS THE BCD VALUE OF THE THUMBWHEEL ADDRESS (N7:7) AND MOVES
IT TO THE PROCESS VARIABLE OF THE PID INSTRUCTION.
THUMBWHEEL N7:7 = PROCESS VARIABLE, (MEASURED VALUE)
 ¦                                                      + FRD ------------------------------- +    ¦
 + ------------------------------------------------------ + FROM BCD                             +  -  +
 ¦                                                      ¦ Source                          N7:7 ¦    ¦
 ¦                                                      ¦                                   80 ¦    ¦
 ¦                                                      ¦ Destination                     N9:0 ¦    ¦
 ¦                                                      ¦                                   50 ¦    ¦
 ¦                                                      + ------------------------------------ +    ¦
 ¦
Rung 2:6
THIS RUNG IS TO ACTIVATE THE THUMBWHEEL SWITCHES.
 ¦                                                      + BTR ------------------------------- +    ¦
 + ------------------------------------------------------ + BLOCK TRANSFER READ                  + -(EN)-+
 ¦                                                      ¦ Rack                             00 ¦    ¦
 ¦                                                      ¦ Group                             2 + -(DN) ¦
 ¦                                                      ¦ Module                            1 ¦    ¦
 ¦                                                      ¦ Control block                   N7:0 + -(ER) ¦
 ¦                                                      ¦ Data file                       N7:5 ¦    ¦
 ¦                                                      ¦ Length                            0 ¦    ¦
 ¦                                                      ¦ Continuous                        Y ¦    ¦
 ¦                                                      + ------------------------------------ +    ¦
```

Figure 23.2. (continued) PID Program.

3. Now proceed to configure the PID module by placing the cursor on the PID instruction and pressing data monitor (F8). Enter the information as shown in figures 23.3 and 23.4.

   Note: See instruction manual for detail specifications on PID parameter descriptions.

4. Observe and enter the data in the following parameters as shown in the PD10.0 control configuration menu of figure 23.3:
   A. Setpoint—Set the first thumbwheel switch (N7:6) to 50.
   B. Process Variable—Set the second thumbwheel switch data (N7:7) to 50.
   C. Error—This displays the difference between the set-point and process variable, with the setpoint at 50 and the process variable at 50, this should read zero.
   D. Bias—Enter a bias of 50%.
   E. gain—Enter a gain of 1.
   F. Reset Time—Enter the maximum amount 3.04e+38. This will eliminate any integral control.
   G. Engineering Unit Maximum—Enter 100.

```
Setpoint:              50.00000    Proportional gain (Kc):        1.000000
Process Var.:          50.00000    Reset Time (Ti) [mins/repeat]: 3.400e+38
Error:                  0.000000   Derivative Rate (Td) [mins]:   0.000000
Output %:              50.00000

Mode:                      AUTO    Deadband:                      0.000000
PV Alarm:                  HIGH    Output Bias %:                50.00000
Deviation Alarm:            POS
Output Limiting:           NONE    Tieback %:                     0.000000
SP Out of Range:             NO    Set Output %:                 50.00000
Error within Deadband:       NO
PID Initialized:            YES

A/M Station Mode:          AUTO
Software A/M Mode:         AUTO
Status Enable (EN):           1
```

Figure 23.3. PID Monitor Menu.

```
PID Equation:      DEPENDENT    Engineering Unit Maximum:      100.0000
Derivative of:            PV    Engineering Unit Minimum:        0.000000
Control Action:        SP-PV
PV Tracking:              NO    Input Range Maximum:           100.0000
                               Input Range Minimum:             0.000000

Update Time (secs):  0.5000000   Output Limit High %:          100.0000
                                 Output Limit Low %:             0.000000

Cascaded Loop:           NO    PV Alarm High:                   0.000000
Cascaded Type:            —    PV Alarm Low:                    0.000000
Master to This Slave:     —    PV Alarm Deadband:               0.000000

                               (+) Deviation Alarm:             0.000000
                               (−) Deviation Alarm:             0.000000
                               Deviation Alarm Deadband:        0.000000
```

Figure 23.4. PID Configuration Menu.

H. Output—gain 3 (SP-PV) + Bias. Your output should display the results of the PID equation. The control output value will be between zero to 100%. For example, a gain of 1 3 SP 50 – PV 50 + Bias 50 = Output of 50%. Output Meter should be at 50% of its scale reading which is five volts.

Experiment with different values in the setpoint and process variable. Observe the output values and compare them with the meter readings.

5. Use your thumbwheel switches to enter various setpoints and process variables parameters. Complete the Data Tables 23.1 and 23.2. Using the example listed above, calculate and record each control voltage output.

Then verify your results with the PID output readings and the meter output readings.

Set the following for Table 23.1:

gain = 1, Bias = 50%, Engineering Max = 100

Table 23.1. Data Table.

Setpoint	Process Variable	Bias %	Output %	Meter Output

Set the following for Table 23.2:

gain = 0.5, Bias = 50%, Engineering Max = 1000

Table 23.2. Data Table.

Setpoint	Process Variable	Bias %	Output %	Meter Output

6. This concludes the project on PID. Don't forget to save and print your program. To test your understanding of the concepts covered in this project, proceed to complete the experiment listed below.

CONTROL LOOP #2

EXPERIMENT 23.1

Name _____ Date _____

Approved by _____

For this experiment, program a second PID control loop and include the use of proportional and integral control. See figure 23.5. Program the following parameters:

1. PID instruction control block PD10:1, Process Variable N7:100, Control Variable N7:25.
2. Program the analog input converter. See Project 22. Set resolution at a maximum of 4095.
3. Program the analog output converter. Use the same block transfer instruction already programmed in Project 23.
4. Set the following parameters: Setpoint = 50; Bias = 50%; Reset time (Integral) = 25; Engineering Maximum = 100; and Update Time = 1.

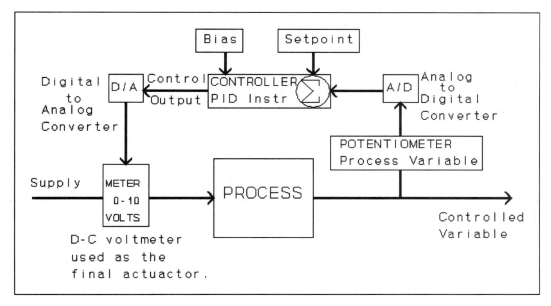

Figure 23.5. Feedback Control Loop 2.

STRUCTURED TEXT

Purpose: To investigate the use of structured text programming.

After completion of this project, you should be able to:
- Convert a basic ladder logic program to structured text programming.
- Investigate the used of a word processor to develop structured text and documentation.

For further information, refer to the following publication: *PLC-5 6200 Series Software; Structured Text User Manual*. Publication 6200-6.4.18. Allen-Bradley.

The programming that we have use up to this point is the ladder logic method of organizing various instructions. Another method of programming various logic instructions is called *structured text*. A structured text program is a series of statements and mnemonics that you can use to perform the same logic functions as with ladder logic. Each logic function is described on a line by line activity with the use of statements or mnemonics.

Structured text can be viewed as another tool in your programming tool pouch helping you work with greater efficiency and productivity. Mastery of these tools develop with extended practice.

Project

This project involves converting a ladder logic program to structured text. WordPerfect word processor will also be used to program and document a structured text program. The program we will use in this project is a simple ladder logic circuit. See figure 24.1. The primary concept will be to write a structured text program to simulate this ladder logic program.

For your first step, review the program shown in figure 24.1. To verify the operation of the circuit, you can program it in ladder logic to see it functioning. The following are the circuit operating steps:
1. This program consists of a toggle switch activating a solenoid ouput. When the starter output coil is energized, TON #1 is activated and begins its timing cycle.
2. The CTU counts the number of timing cycles of TON #1. When the CTU reaches four, it activates a second timer (TON #2) with its done bit.

3. The second timer (TON #2) deenergizes the starter output and resets the CTU with its done bit. The timer enabled bit (EN) also limits the solenoid from activating.

4. Two comparison instructions are included in the circuit, one instruction activates an output light when it is equal to two. The other comparison instruction activates an second output light when it is equal to or greater than three.

PROCEDURES

1. Listed in figure is 24.2 is the structured text program with comments to replace the ladder logic of figure 24.1. The first step is to create a structured file. Then go directly to monitor the structured text file and enter the program directly in the structured text file menu.

   At present, structured text programming software does not allow you to enter any documentations in the structured text format. Therefore, when entering the program directly in the structured text format, you will not be able to enter any descriptive documentations. The side comments are redlined and identified with an apostrophe remark or REM statement to separate them from the structured text. Enter only the structured text instructions listed in figure 24.2.

2. For the next step, proceed to run your program. Turn the toggle switch ON and observe the operation of each line of text. You should notice the timers and the counter text lines. The structured text performs the same functions as the ladder logic in figure 24.1.

3. To include documentations, you must create a source file (duplicate) of the structured text program. The source file is a duplicate of the structured text file which includes descriptive documentations that can be viewed in a printed hard copy or on the monitor with an STX file.

4. To create a source file, proceed to advance editing (F7). Select the rungs of your structured text file (F1), copy (F3), and then copy to your disk (F7). Name the file TEST. This will copy the program as an STX file under the name of TEST.STX

5. You can paste the TEST.STX file back from your disk and enter comments in that format or use a word processing program such as WordPerfect. In WordPerfect, proceed to retrieve the structured text file (TEST.STX). Include as many comments in your program as you prefer. In this format you can also print a hard copy of your file.

   Note: To save the program, use the ASCII TEXT File format (CTRL F5 Text Out in Wordperfect 5.1). Saving the program under this format will allow you to copy it directly in the structured text format. To re-enter the file in the structured text format, use advance editing features pasted from the disk (F8).

6. You will be able to view the STX file with its documentations in the STX format. You can also make documentation changes in the file. But, if you try to accept it to the structured text file (F8), the program will not allow you to transfer. Only structured text will transfer over to the structured text file. To return the structured text file program, press F(8), disregard changes.

7. After you have completed and tested your circuit check with your instructor to verify if your program meets the conditions that are outlined in the project.

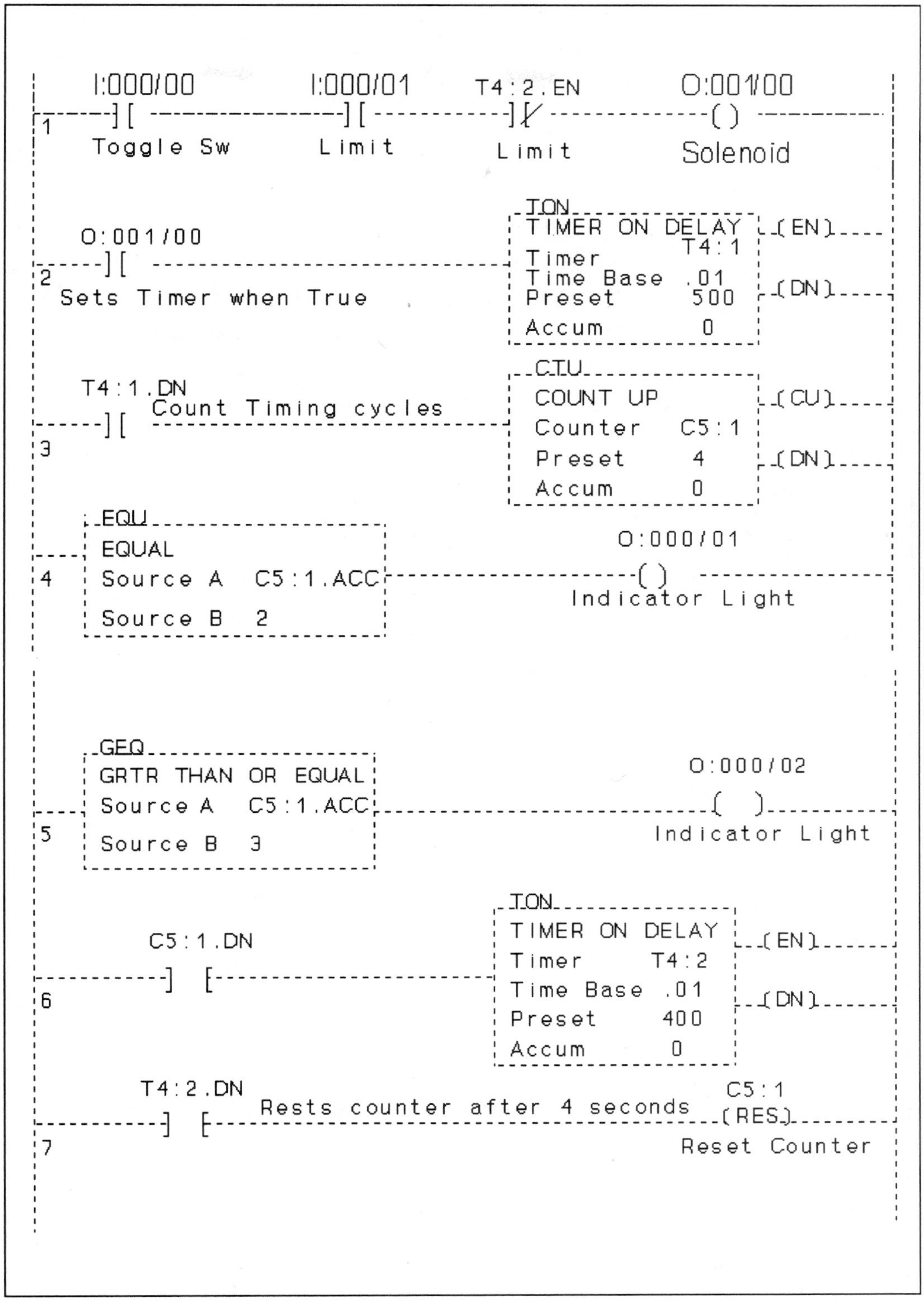

Figure 24.1 Ladder Logic Program for Converting To Text Program.

REM Comments separated with apostrophe ' or REM statement.
'Sol Output. toggle Sw Limit Sw Limit Timer
O:001/00 := I:000/00 AND I:00/01 AND !T4:2.EN;
O:001/00 TON (T4:1, 0.01, 500, 0); 'Starter output activating Timer #1.
T4:1.DN CTU (C5:1, 4, 0); 'Timer #1 done bit activating counter-up.
O:000/01 := C5:1.ACC = 2; ' Output 01 "true" when ctu acc value is equal 2.
O:000/02 := C5:1.ACC >= 3; ' Output bit 02 "true" when ctu acc value >= 3.
C5:1.DN TON (T4:2, 0.01, 400, 0); ' Timer #2 is set by ctu done bit.
T4:2.DN RES (C5:1); ' Counter is reset with timer #2 done bit.

Figure 24.2 Structured Text Program with Documentation

REVIEW

Now that you have successfully completed the first part of Project 24, to test your understanding of the concepts covered in this project, proceed to complete the following experiment.

STRUCTURED TEXT 2

Name _____   Date _____

Approved by _____

Review the ladder logic of Project 10, Figures 10.1 and 10.2 Up/Dn counter. Convert this ladder logic program to structured text. Develop a source file with comments and print a hardcopy.

APPENDIX A

Using This Chapter

Important: For a more detailed description of each of these instructions, see the Allen-Bradley PLC-5 Programming Software Instruction Set Reference, publication 6200-6.4.11.

Courtesy of Allen-Bradley Co., Inc.

Relay Instructions

Instruction		Description
I:012 —] [— 07	Examine On XIC	Examine data table bit I:012/07, which corresponds to terminal 7 of an input module in I/O rack 1, I/O group 2. If this data table bit is set (1), the instruction is true.
I:012 —]/[— 07	Examine Off XIO	Examine data table bit I:012/07, which corresponds to terminal 7 of an input module in I/O rack 1, I/O group 2. If this data table bit is reset (0), the instruction is true.
O:013 —( )— 01	Output Energize OTE	If the input conditions preceding this output instruction on the same rung go true, set (1) bit O:013/01, which corresponds to terminal 1 of an output module in I/O rack 1, I/O group 3.
O:013 —(L)— 01	Output Latch OTL	If the input conditions preceding this output instruction on the same rung go true, set (1) bit O:013/01, which corresponds to terminal 1 of an output module in I/O rack 1, I/O group 3. This data table bit remains set until an OTU instruction resets the bit.
O:013 —(U)— 01	Output Unlatch OTU	If the input conditions preceding this output instruction on the same rung go true, reset (0) bit O:013/01, which corresponds to terminal 1 of an output module in I/O rack 1, I/O group 3. This is necessary to reset a bit that has been latched on.

Courtesy of Allen-Bradley Co., Inc.

Instruction		Description
01 ——(IIN)——	Immediate Input IIN	This instruction updates a word of input-image bits before the next normal input-image update. For a local chassis, program scan is interrupted while the inputs of the addressed I/O group are scanned; for a remote chassis, program scan is interrupted only to update the input image with the latest states as found in the remote I/O buffer.
01 ——(IOT)——	Immediate Output IOT	This instruction updates a word of output-image bits before the next normal output-image update. For a local chassis, program scan is interrupted while the outputs of the addressed I/O group are scanned; for a remote chassis, program scan is interrupted only to update the remote I/O buffer with the latest states as found in the output image.

Timer Instructions

Instruction		Description
TON TIMER ON DELAY Timer T4:1 Time Base 1.0 Preset 15 Accum 0	Timer On Delay TON Status Bits: EN – Enable TT – Timer Timing DN – Done	If the input conditions go true, timer T4:1 starts incrementing in 1-second intervals. When the accumulated value is greater than or equal to the preset value (15), the timer stops and sets the timer done bit.

Rung Condition	EN 15	TT 14	DN 13	ACC Value	TON Status
False	0	0	0	0	Reset
True	1	1	0	increase	Timing
True	1	0	1	>= preset	Done

Instruction		Description
TOF TIMER OFF DELAY Timer T4:1 Time Base .01 Preset 180 Accum 0	Timer Off Delay TOF Status Bits: EN – Enable TT – Timer Timing DN – Done	If the input conditions are false, timer T4:1 starts incrementing in 10 ms intervals as long as the rung remains false. When the accumulated value is greater than or equal to the preset value (180), the timer stops and resets the timer done bit.

Rung Condition	EN 15	TT 14	DN 13	ACC Value	TOF Status
True	1	0	1	0	Reset
False	0	1	1	increase	Timing
False	0	0	0	>= preset	Done

Courtesy of Allen-Bradley Co., Inc.

Instruction		Description
RTO RETENTIVE TIMER ON Timer T4:10 Time Base 1.0 Preset 10 Accum 0	Retentive Timer On RTO Status Bits: EN – Enable TT – Timer Timing DN – Done	If the input conditions go true, timer T4:10 starts incrementing in 1-second intervals as long as the rung remains true. When the rung goes false, the timer stops. If the rung goes true again, the timer continues. When the accumulated value is greater than or equal to the preset (10), the timer stops and sets the timer done bit.

Rung Condition	EN 15	TT 14	DN 13	ACC Value	RTO Status
False	0	0	0	0	Reset
True	1	1	0	increase	Timing
False	0	0	0	maintains	Disabled
True	1	0	1	>= preset	Done

Instruction		Description
T4:1 —(RES)—	Timer Reset RES	If the input conditions go true, timer T4:1 is reset. This instruction resets timers and counters, as well as control blocks. This is necessary to reset the RTO accumulated value.

Counter Instructions

Instruction		Description
CTU COUNT UP Counter C5:1 Preset 10 Accum 0	Count Up CTU Status Bits: CU–Count Up CD–Count Down DN–Count Down one OV–Overflow UN–Underflow	If the input conditions go true, counter C5:1 starts counting, incrementing by 1 every time the rung goes from false-to-true. When the accumulated value is greater than or equal to the preset value (10), the counter sets the counter done bit.

Rung Condition	CU 15	DN 13	OV 12	ACC Value	CTU Status
False	0	0	0	0	Reset
Toggle True	1	0	0	incr by 1	Counting
True	1	1	0	>= preset	Done
True	1	1	1	>32767	Overflow

Instruction		Description
CTD COUNT DOWN Counter C5:1 Preset 10 Accum 35	Count Down CTD Status Bits: CU–Count Up CD–Count Down DN–Count Down one OV–Overflow UN–Underflow	If the input conditions go true, counter C5:1 starts counting, decrementing by 1 every time the rung goes from false-to-true. When the accumulated value is less than the preset value (10), the counter resets the counter done bit.

Rung Condition	CD 14	DN 13	UN 11	ACC Value	CTD Status
False	0	0	0	0	Reset
False	0	1	0	>= preset	Preload
Toggle True	1	1	0	dec by 1	Counting
True	1	0	0	< preset	Done
True	1	0	1	< –32768	Underflow

Courtesy of Allen-Bradley Co., Inc.

Compare Instructions

Instruction		Description

LIM
LIMIT TEST (CIRC)
Low limit N7:10
 3
Test N7:15
 4
High limit N7:20
 22

Limit Test
LIM

If the Test value (N7:15) is >= the Low Limit (N7:10) and <= the High Limit (N7:20), this instruction is true.

Low Limit	Test	High Limit	LIM
0	0	10	T
-5	5	10	T
5	11	10	F
10	0	0	T
10	5	-5	F
10	11	5	T

MEQ
MASKED EQUAL
Source D9:5
 0000
Mask D9:6
 0000
Compare D9:10
 0000

Mask Compare Equal
MEQ

The processor takes the value in the Source (D9:5) and passes that value through the Mask (D9:6). Then the processor compares the result to the Compare value (D9:10). If the result and this comparison values are equal, the instruction is true.

Source	Mask	Compare	MEQ
0008	0008	0009	F
0008	0001	0001	F
0087	000F	0007	T
0087	00F0	0007	F

Courtesy of Allen-Bradley Co., Inc.

Instruction		Description
CMP ───── COMPARE Expression N7:5 = N7:10	Compare CMP	If the expression is true, this input instruction is true. The CMP instruction can perform these operations: equal (=), less than (<), less than or equal (<=), greater than (>), greater than or equal (>=), not equal (<>), and complex expressions (up to 80 characters).

XXX
XXXXXXXXXXXX
Source A　　　N7:5
　　　　　　　　　3
Source B　　　N7:10
　　　　　　　　　1

Source A	Source B	EQU	GEQ	GRT	LEQ	LES	NEQ
10	10	T	T	F	T	F	F
5	6	F	F	F	T	T	T
21	20	F	T	T	F	F	T
-30	-31	F	T	T	F	F	T
-15	-14	F	F	F	T	T	T

Equal to EQU		If the value in Source A (N7:5) is = to the value in Source B (N7:10), this instruction is true.
Greater than or Equal GEQ		If the value in Source A (N7:5) is > or = the value in Source B (N7:10), this instruction is true.
Greater than GRT		If the value in Source A (N7:5) is > the value in Source B (N7:10), this instruction is true.
Less than or Equal LEQ		If the value in Source A (N7:5) is < or = the value in Source B (N7:10), this instruction is true.
Less than LES		If the value in Source A (N7:5) is < the value in Source B (N7:10), this instruction is true.
Not Equal NEQ		If the value in Source A (N7:5) is not equal to the value in Source B (N7:10), this instruction is true.

Courtesy of Allen-Bradley Co., Inc.

Compute Instructions

Instruction	Description
CPT COMPUTE Dest N7:3 3 Expression N7:4 – (N7:6 * N7:10) Compute CPT	If the input conditions go true, evaluate the Expression N7:4 – (N7:6 * N7:10) and store the result in the Destination (N7:3). The CPT instruction can perform these operations: add (+), subtract (–), multiply (*), divide (|), convert from BCD (FRD), convert to BCD (TOD), square root (SQR), logical and (AND), logical or (OR), logical not (NOT), exclusive or (XOR), negate (–), clear (0), and move, X to the power of Y (**), radians (RAD), degrees (DEG), log (LOG), natural log (LN), sine (SIN), cosine (COS), tangent (TAN), inverse sine (ASN), inverse cosine (ACS), inverse tangent (ATN), and complex expressions (up to 80 characters)

Instruction	Description
ACS ARCCOSINE Source F8:19 0.7853982 Dest F8:20 0.6674572 Arc cosine ACS	If input conditions go true, take the arc cosine of the value in F8:19 and store the result in F8:20.

Status Bit	Description
C	always resets
V	sets if overflow is generated; otherwise resets
Z	sets if the result is zero; otherwise resets
S	always resets

Instruction	Description
ADD ADD Source A N7:3 3 Source B N7:4 1 Dest N7:12 4 Addition ADD	When the input conditions are true, add the value in Source A (N7:3) to the value in Source B (N7:4) and store the result in the Destination (N7:12).

Status Bit	Description
C	sets if carry is generated; otherwise resets
V	sets if overflow is generated; otherwise resets
Z	sets if the result is zero; otherwise resets
S	sets if the result is negative; otherwise resets

Courtesy of Allen-Bradley Co., Inc.

Instruction		Description

| ASN
ARCSINE
Source   F8:17
        0.7853982
Dest   F8:18
        0.9033391 | Arc sine
ASN | When input conditions go true, take the arc sine of the value in F8:17 and store the result in F8:18. |

Status Bit	Description
C	always resets
V	sets if overflow is generated; otherwise resets
Z	sets if the result is zero; otherwise resets
S	always resets

| ATN
ARCTANGENT
Source   F8:21
        0.7853982
Dest   F8:22
        0.6657737 | Arc tangent
ATN | When input conditions go true, take the arc tangent of the value in F8:21 and store the result in F8:22. |

Status Bit	Description
C	always resets
V	sets if overflow is generated; otherwise resets
Z	sets if the result is zero; otherwise resets
S	sets if the result is negative; otherwise resets

| AVE
AVERAGE FILE
File   #N7:1
Dest   N7:0
Control   R6:0
Length   4
Position   0 | Average
AVE

Status Bits:
EN – Enable
DN – Done bit
ER – Error Bit | When the input conditions go from false-to-true, add N7:1, N7:2, N7:3, and N7:4. Divide the sum by 4 and store the result in N7:0. |

Status Bit	Description
C	always resets
V	sets if overflow is generated; otherwise resets
Z	sets if the result is zero; otherwise resets
S	sets if the result is negative; otherwise resets

Instruction		Description

| CLR
CLR
Dest　　　D9:34
　　　　　0000 | Clear
CLR | When the input conditions are true, clear decimal file 9, word 34 (set to zero). |

Status Bit	Description
C	always reset
V	always reset
Z	always set
S	always reset

| COS
COSINE
Source　　　F8:13
　　　0.7853982
Dest　　　　F8:14
　　　0.7071068 | Cosine
COS | When input conditions go true, take the cosine of the value in F8:13 and store the result in F8:14. |

Status Bit	Description
C	always resets
V	sets if overflow is generated; otherwise resets
Z	sets if the result is zero; otherwise resets
S	sets if the result is negative; otherwise resets

Courtesy of Allen-Bradley Co., Inc.

Instruction		Description

| DIV ─────
DIVIDE
Source A   N7:3
                          3
Source B   N7:4
                          1
Dest   N7:12
                          3 | Division
DIV | When the input conditions are true, divide the value in Source A (N7:3) by the value in Source B (N7:4) and store the result in the Destination (N7:12). |

Status Bit	Description
C	always resets
V	sets if division by zero or overflow; otherwise resets
Z	sets if the result is zero; otherwise resets
S	sets if the result is negative; otherwise resets

| LN ─────
NATURAL LOG
Source   N7:0
                        5
Dest   F8:20
                 1.609438 | Natural log
LN | When input conditions go true, take the natural log of the value in N7:0 and store the result in F8:20. |

Status Bit	Description
C	always resets
V	sets if overflow is generated; otherwise resets
Z	sets if the result is zero; otherwise resets
S	sets if the result is negative; otherwise resets

| LOG ─────
LOG BASE 10
Source   N7:2
                        5
Dest   F8:3
                0.6989700 | | When input conditions go true, take the log base 10 of the value in N7:2 and store the result in F8:3. |

Status Bit	Description
C	always resets
V	sets if overflow is generated; otherwise resets
Z	sets if the result is zero; otherwise resets
S	sets if the result is negative; otherwise resets

Courtesy of Allen-Bradley Co., Inc.

Instruction		Description

| MUL
MULTIPLY
Source A   N7:3
          3
Source B   N7:4
          1
Dest   N7:12
          3 | Multiply
MUL | When the input conditions are true, multiply the value in Source A (N7:3) by the value in Source B (N7:4) store the result in the Destination (N7:12). |

Status Bit	Description
C	always resets
V	sets if overflow is generated; otherwise resets
Z	sets if the result is zero; otherwise resets
S	sets if the result is negative; otherwise resets

| STD
STANDARD DEVIATION
File   #N7:1
Dest   N7:0
Control   R6:0
Length   4
Position   0 | Standard Deviation
STD

Status Bits:
EN – Enable
DN – Done Bit
ER – Error Bit | When the input conditions go from false-to-true, the elements in N7:1, N7:2, N7:3 and N7:4 are used to calculate the standard deviation of the values and store the result in the Destination (N7:0). |

Status Bit	Description
C	always resets
V	sets if overflow is generated; otherwise resets
Z	sets if the result is zero; otherwise resets
S	always resets

| NEG
NEGATE
Source   N7:3
          3
Dest   N7:12
         –3 | Negate
NEG | When the input conditions are true, take the opposite sign of the Source (N7:3) and store the result in the Destination (N7:12). This instruction turns positive values into negative values and negative values into positive values. |

Status Bit	Description
C	sets if the operation generates a carry; otherwise resets
V	sets if overflow is generated; otherwise resets
Z	sets if the result is zero; otherwise resets
S	sets if the result is negative; otherwise resets

Courtesy of Allen-Bradley Co., Inc.

Instruction		Description

| **SIN** **SINE** Source F8:11 0.7853982 Dest F8:12 0.7071068 | Sine SIN | When input conditions go true, take the sine of the value in F8:11 and store the result in F8:12. |

Status Bit	Description
C	always resets
V	sets if overflow is generated; otherwise resets
Z	sets if the result is zero; otherwise resets
S	sets if the result is negative; otherwise resets

| **SQR** **SQUARE ROOT** Source N7:3 25 Dest N7:12 5 | Square Root SQR | When the input conditions are true, take the square root of the Source (N7:3) and store the result in the Destination (N7:12). |

Status Bit	Description
C	always resets
V	sets if overflow occurs during floating point to integer conversion; otherwise resets
Z	sets if the result is zero; otherwise resets
S	always reset

| **SRT** **SORT** File #N7:1 Control R6:0 Length 4 Position 0 | Sort SRT | When the input conditions go from false-to-true, the values in N7:1, N7:2, N7:3.and N7:4 are sorted into ascending order. |

Courtesy of Allen-Bradley Co., Inc.

Instruction		Description

SUB
SUBTRACT
Source A   N7:3
               3
Source B   N7:4
               1
Dest   N7:12
               2

Subtract
SUB

When the input conditions are true, subtract the value in Source B (N7:4) from the value in Source A (N7:3) and store the result in the Destination (N7:12).

Status Bit	Description
C	sets if borrow is generated; otherwise resets
V	sets if underflow is generated; otherwise resets
Z	sets if the result is zero; otherwise resets
S	sets if the result is negative; otherwise resets

TAN
TANGENT
Source   F8:15
          0.7853982
Dest   F8:16
          1.000000

Tangent
TAN

When input conditions go true, take the tangent of the value in F8:15 and store the result in F8:16.

Status Bit	Description
C	always resets
V	sets if overflow is generated; otherwise resets
Z	sets if the result is zero; otherwise resets
S	sets if the result is negative; otherwise resets

XPY
X TO POWER OF Y
Source A   N7:4
               5
Source B   N7:5
               2
Dest   N7:6
              25

X to the power of Y
XPY

When input conditions go true, take the the value in N7:4, raise it to the power stored in N7:5, and store the result in N7:6.

Status Bit	Description
C	always resets
V	sets if overflow is generated; otherwise resets
Z	sets if the result is zero; otherwise resets
S	sets if the result is negative; otherwise resets

Courtesy of Allen-Bradley Co., Inc.

Logical Instructions

Instruction		Description
AND BITWISE AND Source A D9:3 3F37 Source B D9:4 00FF Dest D9:5 0037	AND	When the input conditions are true, the processor evaluates an AND operation (bit-by-bit) between Source A (D9:3) and Source B (D9:4) and stores the result in the Destination (D9:5). The truth table for an AND operation is: Source A Source B Result 0 0 0 1 0 0 0 1 0 1 1 1
NOT NOT Source A D9:3 00FF Dest D9:5 FF00	NOT Operation	When the input conditions are true, the processor performs a NOT (takes the opposite of) operation (bit-by-bit) on the Source (D9:3) and stores the result in the Destination (D9:5). The truth table for a NOT operation is: Source Destination 0 1 1 0
OR BITWISE INCLUSIVE OR Source A D9:3 3F37 Source B D9:4 00FF Dest D9:5 3FFF	OR	When the input conditions are true, the processor evaluates an OR operation (bit-by-bit) between Source A (D9:3) and Source B (D9:4) and stores the result in the Destination (D9:5). The truth table for an OR operation is: Source A Source B Result 0 0 0 1 0 1 0 1 1 1 1 1
XOR BITWISE EXCLUSIVE OR Source A D9:3 3F37 Source B D9:4 3F37 Dest D9:5 0000	Exclusive OR XOR	When the input conditions are true, the processor evaluates an exclusive OR operation (bit-by-bit) between Source A (D9:3) and Source B (D9:4) and stores the result in the Destination (D9:5). The truth table for an XOR operation is: Source A Source B Result 0 0 0 1 0 1 0 1 1 1 1 0

Status Bit	Description
C	always resets
V	always resets
Z	sets if the result is zero; otherwise resets
S	sets if the most significant bit (bit 15 for decimal or bit 17 for octal) is set (1); otherwise resets

Conversion Instructions

Instruction		Description

FRD —
FROM BCD
Source   D9:3
             0037
Dest   N7:12
             37
	Convert from BCD
	
	FRD
		When the input conditions are true, convert the value in the Source (D9:3) to a integer value and store the result in the Destination (N7:12). The source must be in the range of 0-9999 (BCD).

Status Bit	Description
C	always resets
V	always resets
Z	sets if the destination value is zero; otherwise resets
S	always resets

Instruction		Description

TOD —
TO BCD
Source   N7:3
          44
Dest   D9:5
        0044
	Convert to BCD
	
	TOD
		When the input conditions are true, convert the value in Source (N7:3) to a BCD format and store the result in the Destination (D9:5).

Status Bit	Description
C	always resets
V	sets if the source value is negative or greater than 9999 (i.e. outside of the range of 0-9999)
Z	sets if the destination value is zero; otherwise resets
S	always resets

Instruction		Description

DEG —
RADIANS TO DEGREE
Source   F8:7
    0.7853982
Dest   F8:8
         45
	Convert to Degrees
	
	DEG
		Converts radians (the value in Source A) to degrees and stores the result in the Destination (Source times $180/\pi$).

Status Bit	Description
C	always resets
V	sets if overflow generated; otherwise resets
Z	sets if result is zero; otherwise resets
S	sets if result is negative; otherwise resets

Instruction	Description

RAD —
 DEGREES TO RADIAN
 Source   N7:9
       45
 Dest   F8:10
       0.7853982
	Convert to Radians
	
	 RAD
		Converts degrees (the value in Source A) to radians and stores the result in the Destination (Source times $\pi/180$).

Status Bit	Description
C	always resets
V	sets if overflow generated; otherwise resets
Z	sets if result is zero; otherwise resets
S	sets if result is negative; otherwise resets

Bit Modify and Move Instructions

Instruction	Description

MOV —
 MOVE
 Source   N7:3
       0
 Dest   N7:12
       0
	Move
	 MOV
		When the input conditions are true, move a copy of the value in Source (N7:3) to the Destination (N7:12). This overwrites the original value in the Destination.

Status Bit	Description
C	always resets
V	sets if overflow is generated during floating point–to–integer conversion; otherwise resets
Z	sets if the destination value is zero; otherwise resets
S	sets if result is negative; otherwise resets

MVM —
 MASKED MOVE
 Source   D9:3
       478F
 Mask   D9:5
       00FF
 Dest   D9:12
       008F
	Masked Move
	 MVM
		When the input conditions are true, the processor passes the value in the Source (D9:3) through the Mask (D9:5) and stores the result in the Destination (D9:12). This overwrites the original value in the Destination.

Status Bit	Description
C	always resets
V	always resets
Z	sets if the result is zero; otherwise resets
S	sets if result is negative; otherwise resets

Courtesy of Allen-Bradley Co., Inc.

Instruction		Description
| ```
┌ BTD ─────────────┐
│ BIT FIELD DISTRIB │
│ Source      N7:3  │
│               0   │
│ Source bit    3   │
│ Dest        N7:4  │
│               0   │
│ Dest bit     10   │
│ Length        6   │
└───────────────────┘
``` | Bit Distribute BTD | When the input conditions are true, the processor copies the number of bits specified by Length, starting with the Source bit (3) of the Source (N7:3), and placing the values in the Destination (N7:4), starting with the Destination bit (10). |

File Instructions

Instruction		Description
| ```
┌ FAL ─────────────────┐
│ FILE ARITH/LOGICAL    │
│ Control        R6:1   │
│ Length           8    │
│ Position         0    │
│ Mode           ALL    │
│ Dest         #N15:10  │
│ Expression #N14:0 - 256│
└───────────────────────┘
``` | File Arithmetic and Logic FAL

Status Bits:
EN – Enable
DN – Done Bit
ER – Error Bit | When the input conditions go from false-to-true, the processor reads 8 elements of N14:0, and subtracts 256 (a constant) from each element. This example shows the result being stored in the eight elements beginning with N15:10. The control element R6:1 controls the operation. The Mode determines whether the processor performs the expression on all elements in the files (ALL) per program scan, one element in the files (INC) per scan, or a specific number of elements (NUM) per scan.

The FAL instruction can perform these operations: add (+), subtract (–), multiply (*), divide (|), convert from BCD (FRD), convert to BCD (TOD), square root (SQR), logical and (AND), logical or (OR), logical not (NOT), exclusive or (XOR), negate (–), clear (0), move, and the new math instructions (see the CPT list). |
| ```
┌ FSC ──────────────────┐
│ FILE SEARCH/COMPARE    │
│ Control         R9:0   │
│ Length            90   │
│ Position           0   │
│ Mode              10   │
│ Expression #B4:0 <> #B5:0│
└────────────────────────┘
``` | File Search and Compare FSC

Status Bits:
EN – Enable
DN – Done Bit
ER – Error Bit
IN – Inhibit Bit
FD – Found Bit | When the input conditions go from false-to-true, the processor performs the not-equal-to comparison on 10 elements between files B4:0 and B5:0. The Mode determines whether the processor performs the expression on all elements in the files (ALL) per program scan, one element in the files (INC) per scan, or a specific number of elements (NUM) per scan. The control element R9:0 controls the operation.

When the corresponding source elements are not equal (element B4:4 and B5:4 in this example), the processor stops the search and sets the found .FD and inhibit .IN bits so your ladder program can take appropriate action. To continue the search comparison, you must reset the .IN bit.

To see a list of the available comparisons, see the comparisons listed under the CMP instruction. |

Courtesy of Allen-Bradley Co., Inc.
```

Instruction		Description
COP — COPY FILE Source #N7:0 Dest #N12:0 Length 5	File Copy COP	When the input conditions are true, the processor copies the contents of the Source file (N7) into the Destination file (N12). The source remains unchanged. The COP instruction copies the number of elements from the source as specified by the Length.
FLL — FILL FILE Source N10:6 Dest #N12:0 Length 5	File Fill FLL	When the input conditions are true, the processor copies the value in Source (N10:6) to the elements in the Destination (N12). The FLL instruction only fills as many elements in the destination as specified in the Length.

Diagnostic Instructions

Instruction		Description
FBC — FILE BIT COMPARE Source #I:031 Reference #B3:1 Result #N7:0 Cmp Control R6:4 Length 48 Position 0 Result Control R6:5 Length 10 Position 0	File Bit Compare FBC Status Bits: EN – Enable DN – Done Bit ER – Error Bit IN – Inhibit Bit FD – Found Bit	When the input conditions go from false-to-true, the processor compares the number of bits specified in the Cmp Control Length (48) of the Source file (#I:031) with the bits in the Reference file (#B3:1). The processor stores the results (mismatched bit numbers) in the Result file (#N7:0). File R6:4 controls the compare and file R6:5 controls the file that contains the results. The file containing the results can hold up to 10 (the number specified in the Length field) mismatches between the compared files.
DDT — DIAGNOSTIC DETECT Source #I:030 Reference #B3:1 Result #N10:0 Cmp Control R6:0 Length 20 Position 0 Result Control R6:1 Length 5 Position 0	Diagnostic Detect DDT Status Bits: EN – Enable DN – Done Bit ER – Error Bit IN – Inhibit Bit FD – Found Bit	When the input conditions go from false-to-true, the processor compares the number of bits specified in the Cmp Control Length (20) of the Source file (# I:030) with the bits in the Reference file (#B3:1). The processor stores the results (mismatched bit numbers) in the Result file (#N10:0). Control element R6:0 controls the compare and the control element R6:1 controls the file that contains the results (#N10:0). The file containing the results can hold up to 5 (the number specified in the Length field) mismatches between the compared files. The processor copies the source bits to the reference file for the next comparison. The difference between the DDT and FBC instruction is that each time the DDT instruction finds a mismatch, the processor changes the reference bit to match the source bit. You can use the DDT instruction to update your reference file to reflect changing machine or process conditions.

Instruction		Description
| ```
┌ DTR ─────────────┐
│ DATA TRANSITION  │
│ Source     I:002 │
│ Mask       0FFF  │
│ Reference  N63:11│
└──────────────────┘
``` | Data Transition DTR | The DTR instruction compares the bits in the Source (I:002) through a Mask (0FFF) with the bits in the Reference (N63:11). When the masked source is different than the reference, the instruction is true for only 1 scan. The source bits are written into the reference address for the next comparison. When the masked source and the reference are the same, the instruction remains false. |

Shift Register Instructions

Instruction		Description
| ```
┌ BSL ──────────────┐
│ BIT SHIFT LEFT    │
│ File        #B3:1 │
│ Control     R6:53 │
│ Bit Address I:022/12│
│ Length        5   │
└───────────────────┘
``` | Bit Shift Left BSL<br><br>Status Bits:<br>EN – Enable<br>DN – Done Bit<br>ER – Error Bit<br>UL – Unload Bit | If the input conditions go from false-to-true, the BSL instruction shifts the number of bits specified by Length (5) in File (B3), starting at bit 16 (B3:1/0 = B3/16), to the left by one bit position. The source bit (I:022/12) shifts into the first bit position, B3:1/0 (B3/16). The fifth bit, B3:1/4 (B3/20), is shifted into the UL bit of the control structure (R6:53). |
| ```
┌ BSR ──────────────┐
│ BIT SHIFT RIGHT   │
│ File        #B3:2 │
│ Control     R6:54 │
│ Bit Address I:023/06│
│ Length        3   │
└───────────────────┘
``` | Bit Shift Right BSR<br><br>Status Bits:<br>EN – Enable<br>DN – Done Bit<br>ER – Error Bit<br>UL – Unload Bit | If the input conditions go from false-to-true, the BSR instruction shifts the number of bits specified by Length (3) in File (B3), starting with B3:2/0 (=B3/32), to the right by one bit position. The source bit (I:023/06) shifts into the third bit position B3/34. The first bit (B3/32) is shifted into the UL bit of the control element (R6:54). |
| ```
┌ FFL ──────────────┐
│ FIFO LOAD         │
│ Source      N60:1 │
│ FIFO       #N60:3 │
│ Control     R6:51 │
│ Length        64  │
│ Position       0  │
└───────────────────┘
``` | FIFO Load FFL<br><br>Status Bits:<br>EN – Enable Load<br>DN – Done Bit<br>EM – Empty Bit | When the input conditions go from false-to-true, the processor loads N60:1 into the next available element in the FIFO file, #N60:3, as pointed to by R6:51. Each time the rung goes from false-to-true, the processor loads another element. When the FIFO file (stack) is full, (64 words loaded), the DN bit is set. |
| ```
┌ FFU ──────────────┐
│ FIFO UNLOAD       │
│ FIFO       #N60:3 │
│ Dest        N60:2 │
│ Control     R6:51 │
│ Length        64  │
│ Position       0  │
└───────────────────┘
``` | FIFO Unload FFU<br><br>Status Bits:<br>EU – Enable Unload<br>DN – Done Bit<br>EM – Empty Bit | When the input conditions go from false-to-true, the processor unloads an element from N60:3 into N60:2. Each time the rung goes from false-to-true, the processor unloads another value. All the data in file #N60:3 is shifted one position toward N60:3. When the file is empty, the EM bit is set. |

Courtesy of Allen-Bradley Co., Inc.
```

Instruction		Description
LFL **LIFO LOAD** Source N70:1 LIFO #N70:3 Control R6:61 Length 64 Position 0	LIFO Load LFL Status Bits: EN – Enable Load DN – Done Bit EM – Empty Bit	When the input conditions go from false-to-true, the processor loads N70:1 into the next available element in the LIFO file #N70:3, as pointed to by R6:61. Each time the rung goes from false-to-true, the processor loads another element. When the LIFO file (stack) is full (64 words have been loaded), the DN bit is set.

LFU
 	
LIFO UNLOAD
 	
LIFO   #N70:3
Dest   N70:2
Control   R6:61
Length   64
Position   0
	LIFO Unload
	LFU
	
	Status Bits:
	EN – Enable
	    Load
	EU – Enable
	    Unload
	DN – Done Bit
	EM – Empty Bit
		When the input conditions go from false-to-true, the processor unloads the last element from #N70:3 and puts it into N70:2. Each time the rung goes from false-to-true, the processor unloads another element. When the LIFO file is empty, the EM bit is set.

Sequencer Instructions

Instruction		Description
SQI **SEQUENCER INPUT** File #N7:11 Mask FFF0 Source #I:031 Control R6:21 Length 4 Position 0	Sequencer Input SQI	The SQI instruction compares the Source (#I:031) input image data to a Mask (FFF0) to Reference data (#N7:11) to see if the two files are equal. The operation is controlled by the information in the control file R6:21. When the status of all unmasked bits of the word pointed to by control element R6:21 matches the corresponding reference bits, the rung instruction goes true.
SQL **SEQUENCER LOAD** File #N7:20 Source I:002 Control R6:22 Length 5 Position 0	Sequencer Load SQL Status Bits: EN – Enable DN – Done Bit ER – Error Bit	The SQL instruction loads data into the sequencer File (#N7:20) from the source word (I:002) by stepping through the number of elements specified by Length (5) of the Source (I:002), starting at the Position (0). The operation is controlled by the information in the control file R6:22. When the rung goes from false-to-true, the SQL instruction increments the next step in the sequencer file and loads the data into it for every scan that the rung remains true.
SQO **SEQUENCER OUTPUT** File #N7:1 Mask 0F0F Dest O:014 Control R6:20 Length 4 Position 0	Sequencer Output SQO Status Bits: EN – Enable DN – Done Bit ER – Error Bit	When the rung goes from false-to-true, the SQO instruction increments to the next step in the sequencer File (#N7:1). The data in the sequencer file is transferred through a Mask (0F0F) to the Destination (O:014) for every scan that the rung remains true.

Program Control Instructions

Instruction		Description
——(MCR)——	Master Control Reset MCR	If the input conditions are true, the program scans the rungs between MCR instruction rungs and processes the outputs normally. If the input conditions are false, all non-retentive outputs between the MCR-instruction rung are reset.
10 ——(JMP)——	Jump JMP	If the input conditions are true, the processor skips rungs by jumping to the rung identified by the label (10).
10 ——[LBL]——	Label LBL	When the processor reads a JMP instruction that corresponds to label 10, the processor jumps to the rung containing the label and starts executing. **Important:** Must be the first instruction on a rung.
FOR FOR Label Number 0 Index N7:0 Initial Value 0 Terminal Value 10 Step Size 1	FOR Loop FOR	The processor executes the rungs between the FOR and the NXT instruction repeatedly in one program scan, until it reaches the terminal value (10) or until a BRK instruction aborts the operation. Step size is how the loop is incremented.
NXT NEXT Label Number 0	Next NXT	The NXT instruction returns the processor to the corresponding FOR instruction, identified by the label number specified in the FOR instruction. NXT must be programmed on an unconditional rung that is the last rung to be repeated in a For-Next loop.
——[BRK]——	Break BRK	When the input conditions go true, the BRK instruction aborts a For-Next loop.
JSR JUMP TO SUBROUTINE Program File 90 Input par N16:23 Input par N16:24 Input par 231 Return par N19:11 Return par N19:12	Jump to Subroutine JSR	If the input conditions are true, the processor starts running a subroutine Program File (90). The processor passes the Input Parameters (N16:23, N16:24, 231) to the subroutine and passes Return Parameters (N19:11, N19:12) back to the main program, where the processor encountered the JSR instruction.
SBR SUBROUTINE Input par N43:0 Input par N43:1 Input par N43:2	Subroutine SBR	The SBR instruction is the first instruction in a subroutine file. This instruction identifies Input Parameters (N43:0, N43:1, N43:2) the processor receives from the corresponding JSR instruction. You do not need the SBR instruction if you do not pass input parameters to the subroutine.
RET RETURN ( ) Return par N43:3 Return par N43:4	Return RET	The RET instruction ends the subroutine and stores the Return Parameters (N43:3, N43:4) to be returned to the JSR instruction in the main program.

Courtesy of Allen-Bradley Co., Inc.

Instruction		Description
——[AFI]——	Always False AFI	The AFI instruction disables the rung (i.e., the rung is always false).
——(TND)——	Temporary End TND	If the input conditions are true, the TND instruction stops the processor from scanning the rest of the program (i.e., this instruction temporarily ends the program).
B3 ——[ONS]—— 110	One Shot ONS	If the input conditions preceding the ONS instructions on the same rung go from false-to-true, the ONS instruction conditions the rung so that the output is true for one scan. The rung is false on successive scans.

OSF
ONE SHOT FALLING
Storage Bit   B3/0
Output Bit   15
Output Word   N7:0
	One Shot Falling
	OSF
	
	Status Bits:
	OB – Output
	    Bit ①
	SB – Storage
	    Bit ①
		The OSF instruction triggers an event to occur one time. Use the OSF instruction whenever an event must start based on the change of state of a rung from true-to-false, not on the resulting rung status. The output bit (N7:0/15) is set (1) for one program scan when the rung goes from true-to-false.

OSR
ONE SHOT RISING
Storage Bit   B3/0
Output Bit   15
Output Word   N7:0
	One Shot Rising
	OSR
	
	Status Bits:
	OB – Output
	    Bit ①
	SB – Storage
	    Bit ①
		The OSR instruction triggers an event to occur one time. Use the OSR instruction whenever an event must start based on the change of state of a rung from false-to-true, not on the resulting rung status. The output bit (N7:0/15) is set (1) for one program scan when the rung goes from false-to-true.

SFR SFC Reset Prog File Number 3 Restart Step At	SFC Reset SFR	The SFR instruction resets the logic in a sequential function chart. When the SFR instruction goes true, the processor performs a lastscan/postscan on all active steps and actions in the selected file, and then resets the logic in the SFC on the next program scan. The chart remains in this reset state until the SFR instruction goes false.
——(EOT)——	End of Transition EOT	The EOT instruction should be the last instruction in a transition file. If you do not use an EOT instruction, the processor always evaluates the transition as true.
——(UID)——	User Interrupt Disable UID	The UID instruction temporarily disables an interrupt-driven ladder program (such as an STI or PII) from interrupting the currently executing program.
——(UIE)——	User Interrupt Enable UIE	The UIE instruction re-enables the interrupt-driven ladder program to interrupt the currently executing ladder program.

① These bits are for display purposes only; there is no logical address for them.

Process Control, Message Instructions

Instruction		Description
PID PID Control Block PD10:0 Proc Variable N15:13 Tieback N15:14 Control Output N20:21	Proportional, Integral, and Derivative PID Status Bits: EN – Enable DN – Done Bit (for N control blocks only)	The control block (PD10:0) contains the instruction information for the PID. The PID gets the process variable from N15:13 and sends the PID output to N20:21. The tieback stored in N15:14 handles the manual control station. You can also use N control blocks. If you use PD control block, then there is no done bit. Also, the rung input conditions need to be true.
MSG SEND/RECEIVE MESSAGE Control Block MG7:10	Message MSG	If the input conditions go from false to true, the data is transferred according to the instruction parameters you set when you entered the message instruction. The Control Block (MG7:10) contains status and instruction parameters. You can also use N control blocks. For continuous MSGs, condition the rung to be true for only one scan.

Bit #	Status Bits
15	EN – Enable
14	ST – Start Bit
13	DN – Done Bit
12	ER – Error Bit
11	CO – Continuous
10	EW – Enabled-Waiting
9	NR – No Response
8	TO – Time Out Bit

Courtesy of Allen-Bradley Co., Inc.

Block Transfer Instructions

Integer (N) control block

Word Offset	Description
0	status bits (see below)
1	requested word count
2	transmitted word count
3	file number
4	element number

Block Transfer (BT) control block

Word Mnemonic	Description
.EN thru .RW	status bits
.RLEN	requested length
.DLEN	transmitted word length/error code
.FILE	file number
.ELEM	element number
.RGS	rack/group/slot

Word 0

15	14	13	12	11	10	09	08	07	06	05	04	03	02	01	00
EN	ST	DN	ER	CO	EW	NR	TO	RW	**	rack	**	**	group **	slot	

Instruction		Description
BTR **BLOCK TRANSFER READ** Rack 1 Group 0 Module 0 Control Block N10:100 Data File N10:110 Length 40 Continuous Y	Block Transfer Read BTR	If the input conditions go from false-to-true, a block transfer read is initiated for the I/O module located at rack 1, group 0, module 0. The Control Block (BT10:100 – 6-word file) contains status for the transfer. The Data File (N10:110) is where the data read from the module is stored. The BT Length (40) identifies the number of words in the transfer. A non-continuous block transfer is queued and run only once on a false-to-true rung transition; a continuous block transfer is repeatedly requeued. You can also use the N data type for the control block.

PLC-5/30, -5/40 -5/40E, -5/40L -5/60, -5/60L, -5/80, -5/80E processors		PLC-5/40, -5/40L, -5/60, -5/60L, -5/80, -5/40E, -5/80E processors		PLC-5/60, -5/60L, -5/80, -5/80E processors	
S:7 bit #	BT queue full for rack	S:32 bit #	BT queue full for rack	S:34 bit #	BT queue full for rack
08 ①	0	08	10	08	20
09 ①	1	09	11	09	21
10 ①	2	10	12	10	22
11 ①	3	11	13	11	23
12	4	12	14	12	24
13	5	13	15	13	25
14	6	14	16	14	26
15	7	15	17	15	27

① PLC-5/11, -5/20, and -5/20E processors also

Instruction		Description
BTW **BLOCK TRNSFR WRITE** Rack 1 Group 0 Module 0 Control Block BT10:0 Data File N10:10 Length 40 Continuous Y	Block Transfer Write BTW	If the input conditions go from false-to-true, the block transfer write is initiated for the I/O module located at rack 1, group 0, module 0. The Control Block (BT10:0 – 6-word file) contains status for the transfer. The Data File contains the data to write to the module (N10:10). The BT Length (40) identifies the number of words in the transfer. A non-continuous block transfer is queued and run only once on a false-to-true rung transition; a continuous block transfer is repeatedly requeued. You can also use the N data type for the control block.

ASCII Instructions

Status Bits:
EN – Enable
DN – Done Bit
ER – Error Bit

EM – Empty Bit
EU – Queue
FD – Found Bit

Instruction		Description
ABL **ASCII TEST FOR LINE** Channel 0 Control R6:32 Characters	ASCII Test for Line ABL	If input conditions go from false-to-true, the processor reports the number of characters in the buffer, up to and including the end-of-line characters and puts this value into the position word of the control structure (R6:32.POS). The processor also displays this value in the characters field of the display.
ACB **ASCII CHARS IN BUFFER** Channel 0 Control R6:32 Characters	ASCII Characters in Buffer ACB	If input conditions go from false-to-true, the processor reports the total number of characters in the buffer and puts this value into the position word (.POS) of the control structure. The processor also displays this value in the characters field of the display.
ACI **STRING TO INTEGER CONVERSION** Source ST38:90 Dest N7:123 75	Convert ASCII String to Integer ACI	If input conditions are true, the processor converts the string in ST38:90 to an integer and stores the result in N7:123.

For the ACI instruction:

Status Bit	Description
C	set if source is negative; otherwise resets
V	set if source is >= 32,768 or <= –32,768, otherwise resets
Z	set if source is zero; otherwise resets
S	set if destination is negative; otherwise resets

Courtesy of Allen-Bradley Co., Inc.

Instruction		Description
ACN STRING CONCATENATE Source A ST38:90 Source B ST37:91 Dest ST52:76	ASCII String Concatenate ACN	If input conditions are true, the processor concatenates the string in ST38:90 with the string in ST37:91 and store the result in ST52:76.
AEX STRING EXTRACT Source ST38:40 Index 42 Number 10 Dest ST52:75	ASCII String Extract AEX	If input conditions are true, the processor extracts 10 characters starting at the 42nd character of ST38:40 and store the result in ST52:75.
AIC INTEGER TO STRING CONVERSION Source 876 Dest ST38:42	Convert Integer to ASCII String AIC	If input conditions are true, the processor converts the value 876 to a string and store the result in ST38:42.
AHL ASCII HANDSHAKE LINE Channel 0 AND Mask 0001 OR Mask 0003 Control R6:23 Channel Status	ASCII Handshake Lines AHL	If input conditions go from false-to-true, the processor uses the AND and OR masks to determine whether to set or reset the DTR (bit 0) and RTS (bit 1) lines, or leave them unchanged. Bit 0 and 1 of the AND mask cause the line(s) to reset if 1 and leave the line(s) unchanged if 0. Bit 0 and 1 of the OR mask cause the line(s) to set if 1 and leave the line(s) unchanged if 0.
ARD ASCII READ Channel 0 Dest ST52:76 Control R6:32 String Length 50 Characters Read	ASCII Read ARD Status Bits EN – Enable DN – Done Bit ER – Error Bit UL – Unload EM – Empty EU – Queue	If input conditions go from false-to-true, read 50 characters from the buffer and move them to ST52:76. The number of characters read is stored in R6:32.POS and displayed in the Characters Read Field of the instruction display.
ARL ASCII READ LINE Channel 0 Dest ST50:72 Control R6:30 String Length 18 Characters Read	ASCII Read Line ARL Status Bits EN – Enable DN – Done Bit ER – Error Bit UL – Unload EM – Empty EU – Queue	If input conditions go from false-to-true, read 18 characters (or until end-of-line) from the buffer and move them to ST50:72. The number of characters read is stored in R6:30.POS and displayed in the Characters Read Field of the instruction display.
ASC STRING SEARCH Source ST38:40 Index 35 Search ST52:80 Result 42	ASCII String Search ASC	If input conditions are true, search ST52:80 starting at the 35th character, for the string found in ST38:40. In this example, the string was found at index 42. If the string is not found, the ASCII instruction minor fault bit S:17/8 is set and the result is zero.

Courtesy of Allen-Bradley Co., Inc.

Instruction		Description
ASR ASCII STRING COMPARE Source A ST37:42 Source B ST38:90	ASCII String Compare ASR	If the string in ST37:42 is identical to the string in ST38:90, the instruction is true. Note that this is an input instruction. An invalid string length causes the ASCII instruction error minor fault bit S:17/8 to be set, and the instruction is false.
AWA ASCII WRITE APPEND Channel 0 Source ST52:76 Control R6:32 String Length 50 Characters Sent	ASCII Write Append AWA Status Bits EN – Enable DN – Done Bit ER – Error Bit UL – Unload EM – Empty EU – Queue	If input conditions go from false-to-true, read 50 characters from ST52:76 and write it to channel 0 and append the two character configuration in the channel configuration (default CR/LF). The number of characters sent is stored in R6:32.POS and displayed in the characters sent field of the instruction display.
AWT ASCII WRITE Channel 0 Source ST37:40 Control R6:23 String Length 40 Characters Sent	ASCII Write AWT Status Bits EN – Enable DN – Done Bit ER – Error Bit UL – Unload EM – Empty EU – Queue	If input conditions go from false-to-true, write 40 characters from ST37:40 to channel 0. The number of characters sent is stored in R6:23.POS and displayed in the characters sent field of the instruction display.

Courtesy of Allen-Bradley Co., Inc.

APPENDIX B

Contact Blocks Components

Symbol	Circuit	Description/Notes ❶	Standard			Logic Level	
			Catalog Number			Catalog Number	
			Pressure Terminals	Spade ❷ Terminals		Pressure Terminals	Spade ❷ Terminals
	1 NC	T51 and T51E stack up to 6 blocks (6 circuits) unless otherwise noted.	**10250 T51**	**10250 T59**		**10250 T51E**	**10250 T59E**
	1 NO	T53 and T53E stack up to 6 blocks (6 circuits) unless otherwise noted.	T53	T60		T53E	T60E
	NO - NC	T1 and T1E stack up to 6 blocks (12 circuits) unless otherwise noted.	T1	T40		T1E	T40E
	2 NC	T3 and T3E stack up to 6 blocks (12 circuits) unless otherwise noted.	T3	T42		T3E	T42E
	2 NO	T2 and T2E stack up to 6 blocks (12 circuits) unless otherwise noted.	T2	T41		T2E	T41E
SPECIAL FUNCTION BLOCKS							
	LONC	Late opening NC. Stack up to 6 blocks (6 circuits) unless otherwise noted.	T71	- - -		T71E	- - -
	ECNO-NC	Early closing NO and std. NC. Stack up to 6 blocks unless otherwise noted.	T47	- - -		T47E	- - -
	ECNO-NO	One early closing NO and one standard NO. Not for use on 4 pos. sel. sw., push-pulls or 2 pos. joystick or padlock attachments. Stack up to 4 blocks unless otherwise noted.	T57	- - -		T57E	- - -
	2LONC	2 late opening NC contacts. T45 stackable up to 6 blocks unless otherwise noted.	T45	- - -		T45E	- - -
	LONC-ECNO	Overlapping contacts. Not suitable for use on 4 position selector switch, push-pulls or 2 position joystick or with padlock attachments. Stack up to 4 blocks unless otherwise noted.	T55	- - -		T55E	- - -
	NC (ASP)	Added spring pressure for resistance to shock and vibration. T50 stack up to 6 blocks unless otherwise noted	T50	T61		- - -	- - -
	2 NC (ASP)	Added spring pressure for resistance to shock and vibration. T49 stack up to 6 blocks unless otherwise noted	T49	T91		- - -	- - -
	NO-NC (ASP)	Added spring pressure on NC contact for resistance to shock and vibration. T48 stack up to 6 blocks unless otherwise noted	T48	T62		- - -	- - -
	NO-NC (ST)	Short transit block. Requires less travel to actuate contacts. Stack up to 4 blocks unless otherwise noted.	T92	- - -		- - -	- - -
	2NO-2NC	4 Circuits in single block depth. Rated 300 V max. Not for use on 4 position selector switch or Roto-push. Stack up to 4 blocks unless otherwise noted.	T44	- - -		- - -	- - -

❶ Joy stick, 4 position selector switch and cam code 9 and 15 of Roto-push operators are limited to a maximum of 4 contact blocks. Push-Pull units limited to a maximum of 2 contact blocks.

❷ Limit one per operator. Minimum spacing 2-1/2" centers. Cannot be assembled in standard T-Line enclosures.

Courtesy of Cutler Hammer Co.

ROTO-PUSH® Units Components

DESCRIPTION

A Roto Push control unit combines the function of a push-button and a selector switch. The contacts are operated by the combined action of rotating the outer collar and pushing a button contained in the collar.

Like most other "T" line items, these are listed in two forms — as components for field assembly and the most common types as complete assembled operators.

In selecting the cam and contact blocks for the listed function, the analysis involves considering the function with the collar rotated to the given position with the button free (designated as "N") and then in that same position with the button depressed (designated "D"). This is done for each rotational position of the collar.

Operator and Cam
10250T24111

OPERATOR and CAM

Color and Type of Button	Catalog and Code No.		Cam Code No. Select From Table Below	Price
	Vert. Mtg.	Horiz. Mtg.		
Black Flush	**10250 T241**	**10250 T251**		
Red Flush ❶	**T242**	**T252**		
Green Flush	**T243**	**T253**	1 to 18	$34.20
Black Long	**T261**	**T271**		
Red Long ❶	**T262**	**T272**		
Green Long	**T263**	**T273**		

TABLE 2 CAM AND CONTACT BLOCK SELECTION FOR 2 POSITION SWITCH

Combi-nations	Collar Position ↙ N D	Collar Position ↗ N D	Cam Code 1	Cam Code 2	Cam Code 3	Cam Code 4	Cam Code 5	Cam Code 6	Cam Code 10	Cam Code 11	Cam Code 12	Cam Code 13	Cam Code 14
	Circuit Sequence ❷												
1	0 0	0 X	A ─o o─ NO	A ─o o─ NO	- - -	- - -	A ─o o─ NO	- - -	- - -	A/B NO NO	- - -	- - -	- - -
2	0 0	X 0	- - -	- - -	- - -	A/B NC NO	A/B NC NO	- - -	- - -	A/B NC NO	A ─o o─ NC	A or B NC	A ─o o─ NC
3	0 0	X X	- - -	- - -	- - -	- - -	B ─o o─ NO	A ─o o─ NO	B ─o o─ NO	B ─o o─ NC	- - -	- - -	- - -
4	0 X	0 0	B ─o o─ NO	A/B NC NO	- - -	- - -	- - -	A/B NC NO	A ─o o─ NO	A ─o o─ NO	- - -	- - -	B ─o o─ NO
5	0 X	0 X	A/B NO NO	B ─o o─ NO	- - -	A ─o o─ NO	- - -	- - -	- - -	B ─o o─ NC / A ─o o─ NO	B ─o o─ NO	- - -	- - -
6	0 X	X 0	- - -	- - -	- - -	- - -	- - -	- - -	- - -	- - -	- - -	- - -	A/B NC NO
7	0 X	X X	- - -	- - -	A or B NO	B ─o o─ NO	- - -	B ─o o─ NO	A/B NO NO	A/B NO NO	A/B NC NO	- - -	- - -
8	X 0	0 0	- - -	- - -	A or B NC	B ─o o─ NC	- - -	B ─o o─ NC	A/B NC NC	A/B NC NC	A/B NO NC	- - -	- - -
9	X 0	0 X	- - -	- - -	- - -	- - -	- - -	- - -	- - -	- - -	- - -	- - -	A/B NO NC
10	X 0	X 0	A/B NC NC	B ─o o─ NC	- - -	A ─o o─ NC	- - -	- - -	- - -	A ─o o─ NC	B ─o o─ NC	- - -	- - -
11	X 0	X X	B ─o o─ NC	A/B NO NC	- - -	- - -	- - -	A/B NO NC	A ─o o─ NC	A/B NO NO / B ─o o─ NC	- - -	- - -	B ─o o─ NC
12	X X	0 0	- - -	- - -	- - -	- - -	B ─o o─ NC	A ─o o─ NC	B ─o o─ NC	A/B NO NC	- - -	- - -	- - -
13	X X	0 X	- - -	- - -	- - -	A/B NO NC	A ─o o─ NO	- - -	- - -	A/B NO NC	A ─o o─ NO	A or B NO	A ─o o─ NO
14	X X	X 0	A ─o o─ NC	A ─o o─ NC	- - -	- - -	A ─o o─ NC	- - -	- - -	A/B NC NC	- - -	- - -	- - -

❶ Not to be used for emergency stop applications.
❷ N = Button in free or normal position. D = Button depressed.

Courtesy of Cutler Hammer Co.

Contact Blocks Components

TABLE 2A CAM AND CONTACT BLOCK SELECTION FOR 3 POSITION SWITCH

ROTO-PUSH Operator
with Flush Button
and Assembled withd
Legend Plate
Contact Block and
Legend Plate

ROTO-PUSH Operator
with Long Button
and Assembled with
Contact Block and
Legend Plate

Series Connection:
A — NO
B — NC

Parallel Connection:
A — NO
B — NC

The connections are not made at the factory. They are illustrated in the selection table as requirements, but must be made on the job.

Combinations	Collar Position ↖ N D	Collar Position ↑ N D	Collar Position ↗ N D	Cam Code 7	Cam Code 8 ❶	Cam Code 9	Cam Code 15	Cam Code 16	Cam Code 17	Cam Code 18
1	0 0	0 0	0 X	A NO / B NO	A NC / B NO	---	B NO ❶	B NO	---	A NC / B NO
2	0 0	0 0	X X	---	---	B NO	---	---	A NO	---
3	0 0	0 X	0 0	---	---	A NO / B NC ❶	---	---	---	A NO / B NO
4	0 0	0 X	0 X	---	---	---	---	---	---	B NO
5	0 0	0 X	X X	---	---	A NO ❶	---	---	---	---
6	0 0	X X	0 0	---	A NO / B NO	---	---	---	---	---
7	0 0	X X	0 X	---	B NO	---	---	---	---	---
8	0 0	X X	X 0	A NC / B NO	---	---	---	---	---	---
9	0 0	X X	X X	B NO	---	---	---	---	---	---
10	0 X	0 0	0 0	A NO / B NC	A NO / B NO	---	A NO ❶	A NO	B NO	A NO / B NC
11	0 X	0 0	0 X	A NO	---	---	A NO / B NO ❶	A NO / B NO	---	---
12	0 X	0 0	X X	---	---	---	---	---	A NO / B NO	---
13	0 X	0 X	0 0	---	---	---	---	---	A NO	---
14	0 X	0 X	0 X	---	---	---	---	---	---	A NO / B NO
15	0 X	X X	0 0	---	A NO	---	---	---	---	---
16	0 X	X X	0 X	---	A NO / B NO	---	---	---	---	---
17	0 X	X X	X X	A NO / B NO	---	---	---	---	---	---
18	X 0	0 0	0 0	A NC / B NC	---	---	---	---	---	---
19	X 0	0 0	X X	---	A NC	---	---	---	---	---
20	X 0	0 0	X 0	---	A NC / B NC	---	---	---	---	---
21	X 0	X X	0 0	---	---	---	---	---	A NC / B NC	---
22	X 0	X X	X X	A NC / B NO	A NC / B NC	---	---	A NC	B NC	A NC / B NO
23	X 0	X X	X 0	A NC	---	---	---	A NC / B NC	---	---
24	X 0	X 0	X 0	---	---	---	A NC / B NC	---	---	A NC / B NC
25	X 0	X 0	X X	---	---	---	A NC ❶	---	---	A NC
26	X X	0 0	0 0	B NC	---	A NC ❶	---	---	---	---
27	X X	0 0	0 X	A NO / B NC	---	---	---	---	---	---
28	X X	0 0	X 0	---	B NC	---	---	---	---	---
29	X X	0 0	X X	---	---	A NC / B NO ❶	---	---	---	---
30	X X	X X	0 0	---	---	B NC	---	---	A NC	---
31	X X	X X	X 0	A NC / B NC	A NO / B NC	---	---	B NC	---	A NO / B NC
32	X X	X 0	X 0	---	---	---	B NC ❶	---	---	B NC
33	X X	X 0	X X	---	---	---	A NO / B NC ❶	---	---	A NC / B NC

❶ Limited to 4 contact blocks.
❷ N = Button in free or normal position.
  D = Button depressed.

Courtesy of Cutler Hammer Co.

Entering Step/Transition Pairs

Steps and transitions are entered in pairs. The SFC editor only lets you enter correct step and transition pairs. See the examples below for samples of correct step/transition pairs.

Important: All transition files must include a conditioned EOT (End of Transition) instruction. If you do not include an EOT instruction, the processor automatically evaluates the transition file as true.

The examples in this chapter show the steps you would perform if your program files have already been created. For more information about creating program files, see "Using Undefined Program Files" on page 9-4.

Figure 9.1 shows you how to enter a simple step and transition. To enter these SFC structures, start on the SFC Edit selections screen. For more complex SFC structures, see chapter 11.

Figure 9.1
Entering a Simple Step/Transition on a Classic PLC-5 Processor

To Get This:	Follow this Procedure:
Simple Step/Transition Pair	[F3] – Append Step/Transition
	or
	[F4] – Insert Step/Transition
	Move cursor to step program file you want
	[F1] – Select Step
	Move cursor to transition program file you want
	[F2] – Select Transition
	[Enter] to return to the SFC Edit selections
	[F9] – Config/Build
	[F10] – Build Chart

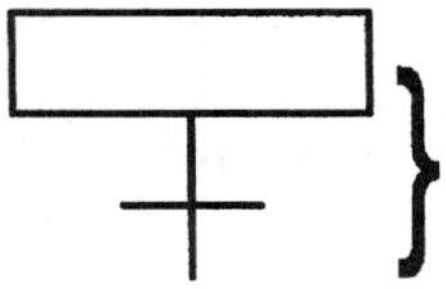

Table 9.A describes the tasks you can perform on the Assigning Ladder Logic screen (appending or inserting a step/transition).

Table 9.A
Available Tasks on the Assigning Ladder Logic Screen

If You Want to:	Press this Key:
Select the highlighted file number for the current step	[F1] – Select Step
Select the highlighted file number for the current transition	[F2] – Select Transition
If you have multiple steps and transitions in the current structure (branch), move the cursor to the next step or transition	[F3] – Next Step/Transition
Delete the cursored program file	[F5] – Delete File
Create a program file	[F6] – Create File
Change the name of the highlighted program file	[F10] – Change File Name

Courtesy of Allen Bradley Co., Inc.

Creating Selection and Simultaneous Branches

To create branches, follow the steps below:

Figure 9.2
Entering a Selection Branch Step/Transition on a
Classic PLC-5 Processor

To Get this:	Follow this Procedure:
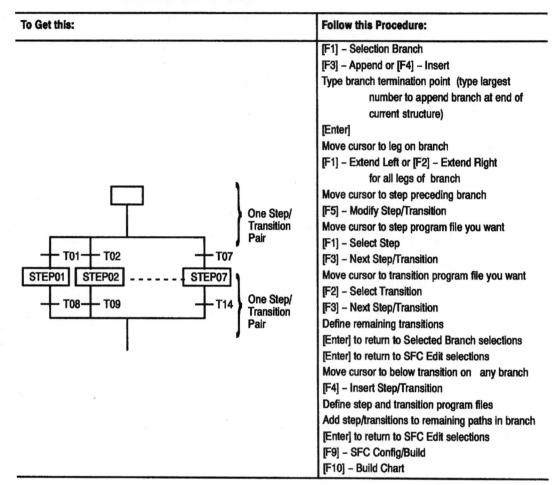	[F1] – Selection Branch
	[F3] – Append or [F4] – Insert
	Type branch termination point (type largest number to append branch at end of current structure)
	[Enter]
	Move cursor to leg on branch
	[F1] – Extend Left or [F2] – Extend Right for all legs of branch
	Move cursor to step preceding branch
	[F5] – Modify Step/Transition
	Move cursor to step program file you want
	[F1] – Select Step
	[F3] – Next Step/Transition
	Move cursor to transition program file you want
	[F2] – Select Transition
	[F3] – Next Step/Transition
	Define remaining transitions
	[Enter] to return to Selected Branch selections
	[Enter] to return to SFC Edit selections
	Move cursor to below transition on any branch
	[F4] – Insert Step/Transition
	Define step and transition program files
	Add step/transitions to remaining paths in branch
	[Enter] to return to SFC Edit selections
	[F9] – SFC Config/Build
	[F10] – Build Chart

Courtesy of Allen Bradley Co., Inc.

Figure 9.3
Entering a Simultaneous Branch Step/Transition on a
Classic PLC-5 Processor

To Get this:	Follow this Procedure:
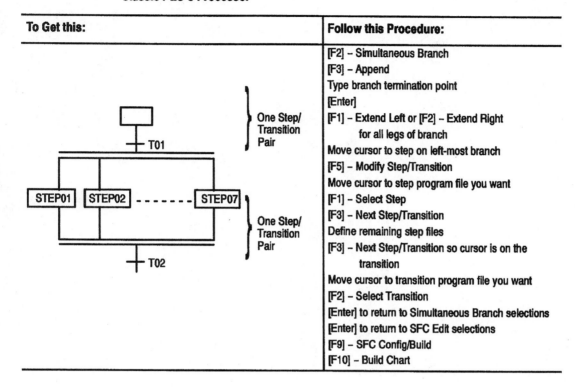	[F2] – Simultaneous Branch
	[F3] – Append
	Type branch termination point
	[Enter]
	[F1] – Extend Left or [F2] – Extend Right
	for all legs of branch
	Move cursor to step on left-most branch
	[F5] – Modify Step/Transition
	Move cursor to step program file you want
	[F1] – Select Step
	[F3] – Next Step/Transition
	Define remaining step files
	[F3] – Next Step/Transition so cursor is on the
	transition
	Move cursor to transition program file you want
	[F2] – Select Transition
	[Enter] to return to Simultaneous Branch selections
	[Enter] to return to SFC Edit selections
	[F9] – SFC Config/Build
	[F10] – Build Chart

Courtesy of Allen Bradley Co., Inc.

INDEX